KT-504-587

The Permaculture Plot

Compiled by
Simon Pratt

Permanent Publications

Published by
Permanent Publications
Hyden House Limited
Little Hyden Lane
Clanfield
Hampshire
PO8 0RU
England
Tel: (0705) 596500
Fax: (0705) 595834

© 1994 Simon Pratt

Design and typesetting by
Tim Harland, Permanent Publications

Cover photograph
Tim Harland, Hyden House (*see page 77*)

Printed by
Woolnough Bookbinding Limited
Irthlingborough, Northamptonshire

British Library Cataloguing in Publication Data
A catalogue record for this book is available from the British Library

ISBN 1 85623 007 4

A voluntary Tree Tax on the paper used in the production of this book is paid
into a special fund for tree planting projects. Submissions for grants may be
made to the Permaculture Association (Britain). Grants are available for seed
and tree stock only.

All rights reserved. No part of this publication may be reproduced, stored in
a retrieval system, rebound or transmitted in any form or by any means,
electronic, mechanical, photocopying, recording or otherwise, without the
prior written permission of Hyden House Limited.

Content

Illustrations

All photographs and illustrations have been supplied from source except those on the following pages which have been supplied, or redrawn from originals, by:

Simon Pratt   25, 35, 37, 45, 47, 51, 61
Chris Hoppe   65, 82, 90
Tim Harland   74, 88
Tiffany Robinson   31 (profile), 40, 64
All key overlays to plans by Tim Harland
Cartoon on page 10 by Rob Hopkins

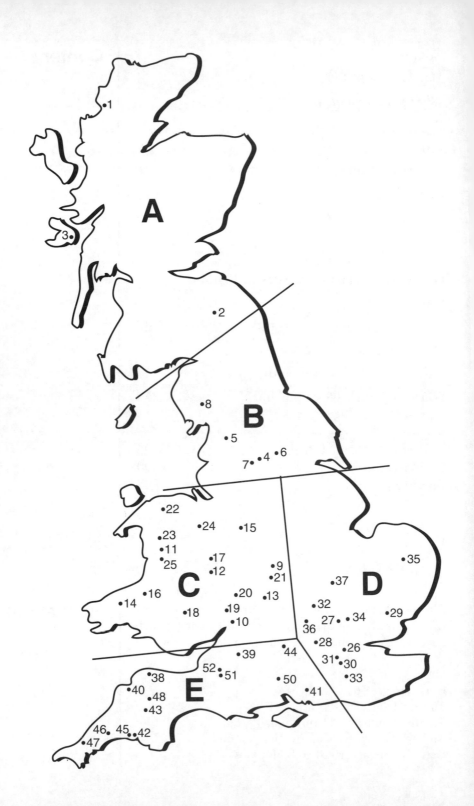

Key to Permaculture Sites
in Britain

What is Perma-culture?

Permaculture (**permanent agriculture** or **permanent culture**) is the conscious design of sustainable human habitats. It is based on co-operating with Nature and caring for the Earth and its people.

Permaculture draws together the skills and knowledge of many ecologically sound disciplines – from traditional to modern – to create ways of providing for our needs, including food, shelter and financial and social structures.

The principles and practice of permaculture can be used by anyone, anywhere:

- ❀ City flats, yards and window boxes
- ❀ Suburban and country houses/gardens
- ❀ Allotments and smallholdings
- ❀ Farms and estates
- ❀ Countryside and conservation areas
- ❀ Commercial and industrial premises
- ❀ Educational establishments
- ❀ Waste ground...

Permaculture empowers the individual to be resourceful, self-reliant and a conscious part of the solution to the many problems facing us, both locally and globally.

Preface

Welcome to the third edition of *The Permaculture Plot*. I am pleased to present 52 examples of permaculture design principles being put into practice on these islands. If you come across any more worthy of inclusion, please let me know. I have not adopted any selection criteria in compiling this directory: I have not personally visited all the sites, although many are known to me. Many are in the early stages of development, so do not expect to see wonderful flourishing productive systems. I hope they all indicate a way out of our current dilemmas as an over-consuming society, towards a saner, sensible, sustainable future.

Most entries have been reprinted as the contributors have written them, with minor grammatical changes. In some cases significant editing was necessary in order to fit the page, but the words are still those of the contributors, to whom many thanks are due.

With very few exceptions, visitors are welcome at all the sites listed. Please do read the accompanying notes and articles before setting out on your journey of exploration. I did ask all the contributors to the last edition whether visitors had been a hassle or a help overall. They were asked to provide a 'score' on a scale of 1 (hassle) to 5 (helpful). From 24 responses, the average score was 3.83, so my conclusion is that visitors are genuinely welcomed by the people listed in this guide!

Permaculture does seem to be catching on in this country: the last edition of this publication listed 33 sites and projects, of which 25 have repeated or updated their entries this time round. The first edition of *The Permaculture Plot*, published by the Permaculture Association in 1985, listed a mere seven projects! So I look forward to a 1996/7 edition with at least 80 entries (with your help) – *see page 93 for further details.*

Simon Pratt
Compiler
December 1993

Editorial Address
*Redfield Community
Buckingham Road
Winslow
BUCKINGHAM
MK18 3LZ*

Telephone
(0296) 712161

Visiting Sites

Many of these sites are not public. Do not under any circumstances visit these without arranging to do so first, by phoning or writing. Be warned: I have had to turn people away who arrived unannounced! Public sites will usually have an entrance fee, which may vary from time to time. People who do not charge may equally appreciate a gift to thank them for their time and effort, or an equal amount of your time doing a useful job. Please respect the views of someone who says they are not available to see you.

If you visit these sites people may wish to hear your views, or they may simply be willing to show you their work. Do not expect people to want to hear from you "how they could be doing it better". They often have a very clear picture of that themselves and are just working through their priorities.

Please respect the privacy and time of people you contact.

Information has been provided to make visiting these sites as straightforward as possible.

BA means you may visit the site by arrangement with the contact person. If there is a note to say there is no accommodation, please make your own arrangements.

WWOOF means you may visit as a member of the national organisation, Working Weekends On Organic Farms. WWOOF is a countrywide exchange network where bed and board and practical experience are given in return for work on organic farms and smallholdings. Midweek, long term and overseas stays are also available. Excellent opportunities for organic training or changing to a rural life. Annual subscription £8 to the Membership Secretary, WWOOF, 19 Bradford Road, Lewes, East Sussex BN7 1RB.

The Ideal WWOOFer

The ideal WWOOFer

- is content to work alone for several hours on one job, appreciating the meditation and rhythm it provides, without complaining of boredom

- finds the space and quiet of the countryside comfortable and refreshing

- enjoys their own company and is intent on developing a sense of humour when with others

- susses things out by looking and listening and sometimes taking initiatives

- is sensitive enough to see that intellectual discussions can be energy drains at midnight

- refrains from constantly demanding "what next?" or "why?" and appreciates that farming is 'all go' or 'rest while you can'!

- recognises that WWOOF hosts are human beings with failures and fatigue

- knows that spades should not be used as levers for boulders and that fixing them is yet another chore, another expense

- works out that if five people share the same house, chances are that the solid fuel central heating will only provide enough water for one bath each and two loads in the washing machine a week AND this is ecologically sound

M any City Farms and Community Gardens have been following permaculture principles for years, some without realising it. Our method of agriculture is socially, environmentally and ecologically sound. People, plants, animals and the land become interdependent. We adopt conservation principles; we recycle many different materials and we design our projects to be as diverse as possible.

City Farms and Community Gardens are not conventional food-producing enterprises where the growing of crops and the raising of livestock is an end in itself. They are community projects. They create a stimulating environment and offer people opportunities that they would not experience otherwise. Some Farm and Garden projects have been going for nearly 20 years. People in several local communities set them up on derelict or under-used land in the inner city, on the urban fringe, or in new towns. There are now over 60 Farms at various stages of development and there are examples in most major cities in Britain.

These projects offer everyone a place to grow things and tend animals – it allows them to experience a wide range of rural activities and help manage the project on behalf of the community. City Farming is, therefore, of a peculiar nature, offering social welfare, environmental, employment, recreational and educational opportunities, as well as economic ones. Organic principles are usually followed because the people attracted to City Farming and Gardening are 'conservation conscious', and because in our situation ecological actions do work and are seen as necessary if sites are to thrive.

City Farms are faced with the same problems as other producers, but have other pressures too. On many, the soil is thin or stony, contaminated by various chemical or physical wastes.

Some sites are steeply sloping, poorly drained or infertile. Most are small in size, the average being 4.1 acres (0.5 to 90 acres). This small acreage has many demands placed upon it – pastures for livestock; cropping ground; areas for wildlife or educational work; play space; composting and recycling areas, to name but a few.

City Farms

Address
National Federation of City Farms
93 Whitby Road
Brislington
BRISTOL
BS4 3QF

Telephone
(0272) 719109

Then there are the human problems involved in managing a complex enterprise that co-ordinates core staff, volunteers, temporary employment and training schemes and a variety of placements. We have had to find ways of overcoming these limitations to make work easier and the projects succeed.

By adopting the principles of sustainable agriculture we have found that some tasks are easier to perform, the environment is improved, costs are reduced and productive cropping achieved on previously derelict sites.

Our husbandry aims are to:

- **Promote welfare** of people, animals and the environment, especially the land.
- **Be self-sustaining**, replenishing the soil, keeping insect numbers in balance through natural control.
- **Recycle resources** by composting, feeding discarded wastes to animals and salvaging timber.
- **Plan intensively** to produce as much from the land as possible.
- **Encourage diversity** by keeping a wide range of animals, growing a large collection of plants and developing diverse micro-climates by contouring, using windbreaks etc..
- **Integrate techniques** by bringing different disciplines together, such as ecology and architecture, introducing stock into gardens etc..
- **Save energy** by using appropriate technology, zoning the site, using natural fertilisers.

Permaculture is actively promoted by the National Federation of City Farms (NFCF). It began formally in 1984, when we arranged courses by Bill Mollison and Sego Jackson. These gave inspiration and helped us to structure the various ideas that had been evolving.

As a result of these courses, permaculture is covered in NFCF technical literature and periodicals. The principles are often central to the feasibility studies we conduct for new groups and established projects interested in developing their site to its fullest potential. In addition, permaculture applications are covered in training workshops that are run regularly throughout the country and in community gardening courses.

Some examples of City Farming practices include:

- Collecting roof water run off for watering in greenhouses.
- Animal shelters set into banks or grassed on their sides and roofs.
- Spiral herb gardens to cultivate both shade and sun loving plants in a limited space.
- Growing potatoes in stacks of old tyres for demonstration of patio/balcony growing techniques.
- 'Chicken tractor' giving poultry access to small runs radiating from central housing, with rotation of cropping.

The NFCF itself will be constructing a timber office and demonstration centre in Bristol during 1994 which will incorporate a number of permaculture ideas, and will be completely covered with a grass roof.

Difficulties Putting Permaculture into Practice

The time factor: When people come up with an idea for a City Farm, there is a great deal of initial enthusiasm. The legal aspects, fund-raising and project organisation can take a long time – perhaps 18 months or 2 years. By the time the land is made available, people's enthusiasm may have been dampened, so activities that yield a quick success are important.

Attitudes: It's true that people will do what they know best. Radical approaches will not be accepted unless the case is expertly sold and adequate back-up support is available. Unfortunately, there are few people with permaculture expertise in this country in the right places, who can support a voluntary group regularly over a long period.

Priorities: Projects are always short of money and this affects working practices and priorities. Everything else seems to take precedence over site landscaping because needs are more immediate: the construction of animal houses, for example.

Survival: Projects are under pressure in many areas as local authorities review their land stocks. A few sites are threatened with development. For some projects, day-to-day concern is with immediate survival, rather than with establishing a long term agro-ecosystem.

The City Farm Sites

A City Farm is a highly complex development. It will consist of many separate components, all of which have to be integrated successfully. Each site can have more than a dozen uses. On a very small area of land, as most projects are, many of the demands might conflict:

- recreational activities
- educational schemes
- nature projects
- livestock husbandry
- fodder production
- children's pursuits (play/learning)
- individual's needs (sanctuary/therapy)
- social events (open days, fairs)
- business operations (shop, café, market garden)
- community festivals
- environmental improvement (landscaping, forestry)
- gardening

To make the most of available land, we follow these tenets:

- use what you've got – turn a disadvantage into an advantage;
- design elements to have many functions – if you can't find five uses for doing something, should you really be doing it?

As an example of the former, rather than draining a marshy hollow and turning it into pasture, we might use the area for wildlife, grow rushes for animal bedding, or produce aquatic plants as fertiliser and fodder.

Where possible, each element is given many different functions – over 18 for a hedge, for example. Similarly, site landscaping materials can also be used for animal fodder, pollen and nectar sources for bees, amenity, wildlife sanctuary and biomass for composting.

A field can be used as a pasture for animals to graze, exercise and be displayed and as recreational space. If sown with wild herbs the field can then become an attractive picnic area and the herbs will be eaten as medicines and tonics on-the-hoof. It could also be developed as a wild flower conservation meadow. With careful management, this one paddock can be developed to possess more than five functions and the value of that land to the project is increased many fold.

The Future
Many City Farms have the potential to develop as community businesses. Already set up are market gardens, cafés, shops and business starter units. In each case, income from these enterprises is returned to the neighbourhood City Farm project to support its social welfare and educational roles.

Also being considered is the use of Farms as neighbourhood distribution networks. A City Farm could link with a rural organic smallholder who would grow a range of products under contract. This food would then be made available to nearby households, which might participate in the scheme on a co-operative basis.

Plant a Seed and Grow a Community

National Federation of City Farms

15

WHATEVER HAPPENED TO...?

In any publication of this nature there will be changes as people move on or direct their energies elsewhere. Just for the record, I am including brief notes on those entries which appeared in the last edition (January 1991), but which do not appear this time round. It is remarkable that it is only eight of those 33 entries.

Beau Champ: This project – "18 acres of mixed woods (oak, chestnut and pine), meadows and vines" – is now underway near the Dordogne in south-west France. Contact: Laurence Snook, Beau Champ, Montpey Roux, 24610 Villefranche de Lonchat, France. Telephone (010-33) 65 37 36 17.

Dovecot: Ian Lillington has moved to Australia for a while and the current residents have decided not to maintain the entry.

Lees Stables: Things have not worked out for the group which moved to Coldstream in 1988. Nancy and Graham expect to be moving on during the currency of this publication. I report this with some sadness as I feel that the Lees Stables was one of the outstanding examples of cool temperate permaculture. We can only hope that the next residents will want to continue maintaining the systems established in the last five years. It will certainly be a test of the resilience of these systems! Nancy has written a piece based on their experiences, which appears on the next page.

Llandruidion: Rob and Gill Dowsett have found the stream of visitors a little wearing and have declined the invitation to be included this time round. Please let them have a well earned rest!

Micro-Robotics: Peter Miller has decided that an entry is no longer appropriate.

Shepway Allotments: Caroline Morgan has been evicted from her allotment in Maidstone! (*See next page*).

The Holt: Yohanna Gardener has finally sold her house and garden.

Tocher Knowe: Sadly, Bruce Marshall, pioneer of peat hill and bog reclamation for grazing through encouraging earthworms, has now died.

WE ALL NEED TO COMMUNICATE WELL
Nancy Woodhead

We have had a large number of enquiries through the entry in *The Permaculture Plot*, as well as from other sources. Many come without a s.a.e.! However, the majority are efficient and polite and generally useful. The letter as the first introduction is important and should contain enough information to ensure that the reply does not require too many personal enquiries to be made, i.e. so that a photocopied letter can be used in reply to explain what visitors can expect. This is helpful to reduce admin. and keep errors and omissions to a minimum.

Having said that, of the people who have visited, there have been many successes. Occasional letdowns on both sides are due to poor communication of expectations. And then the others which don't work out are due to the unavoidable (?) phenomenon that visitors and residents have things on their agendas outside the new relationship which is being made. Many people coming through *The Permaculture Plot* are searching for something other than a place to work and stay for a few days. Some are looking for therapy, some for inspiration, some for 'The Answer', often just for something new and different. Sometimes they get what they want and so do we but other times it never becomes clear what is wanted from the relationship and the experience is a disappointment from one or both points of view. For this to be avoided, people need to be clear about what they want and what is being offered. On both sides. For this to happen, we all need to communicate well, especially about 'where we are coming from'.

TROUBLE ON THE ALLOTMENT
Caroline Morgan

Shortly after submitting the entry for the previous edition, I was evicted from my allotments. I was under the misapprehension that the Maidstone Allotments Management Committee (a non-elected body, which can co-opt and remove members, myself included) would have to get a court order to carry out the eviction. The Management Committee said that I was infringing my agreement by keeping bees, and having weeds, pests and diseases, which I disputed. I had also had a verbal assurance from the Chairman that I would hear no more if I moved all the bees onto the middle allotment, which I did. However, as he would put nothing in writing it was impossible to prove. He also suggested that I put the bees on vacant allotments, which I was reluctant to do without written permission, which was not forthcoming.

As the allotments are Council owned, I thought that it would be the arbiter in any dispute about the inter-pretation of the agreement. However, a small group of Councillors on the Allotments Advisory Group decided that the Management Committee would be solely respon-sible for the management of allotments. Whilst I was still going through the official channels, trying to resolve the situation, the Management Committee put my bees and equipment into black sacks (in the middle of winter) and dumped them in some Council gardens.

Even though the bees were no longer on site the Management Committee turned up and destroyed a cold frame, removed equipment and plants, cut a fine specimen of a standard tree which was self-sown and, worst of all, started a bonfire on an adjacent vacant allotment and burned my compost and wildlife shelter along with all the worms and mini-beasts.

Having nothing left to fight for, I gave up to divert my energies to other things. Shortly after I was evicted all the other plots became vacant due to vandalism. The site is criticised by local residents because of its derelict nature. The Council will probably come to an arrangement with a Housing Association to build on the site and the Allotment Management Committee will probably get a sum of money for giving up the site.

D uartbeg is set in the essential shelter of the most northwesterly remnant of native oak woodland in Scotland, a 200 acre National Nature Reserve protected within a 700 acre sheep and deer exclosure. Emma and Bernard rent the house and land and started the nursery as part of the vision and task of reforesting the land. Seeds of all the native tree and shrub species are collected locally and grown organically, producing up to 80,000 trees annually which are then planted out on sites all over the north-west as shelterbelts and small multi-purpose woods. Some go to the RSPB reserve Isle Martin, off Ullapool, where Emma and Bernard have been working on woodland restoration since 1981. Some will go into a recently bought 81 acre forest that they are converting from conifer plantation to forest garden. At present they are clearing rhododendron, thinning, converting and building with logs, learning and designing.

At Duartbeg an old dyked garden by the sea has developed into a productive, well-mulched hidden fruit and vegetable jungle; carrots and potatoes are grown on a peat bog with the chickens, ducks and doves and the polytunnel has a solar shower and a strawberry and turf-roofed port. Permaculture design has been important in this development. The charity Reforesting Scotland, working to restore the land and communities through reforestation, is also based and produces its biannual journal here – further enquiries with s.a.e. welcomed.

Workers and visitors are accommodated at Duartbeg in a purpose-built self-contained bothy and a caravan, supplied with wholefoods from the house, garden and environs. They are expected to help with a wide variety of seasonal work – seed gathering, nursery work, building, wood-chopping, weeding trees, forest and garden work, being with the three homeschooled children and helping in the studio and office. Graphic, artistic, secretarial and Apple Mac skills are extra welcome!

SCOTLAND

1

Duartbeg

Address
Duartbeg
Scourie
LAIRG
Sutherland
IV27 4TJ

Telephone
(0971) 502406

Contact
Emma & Bernard
Planterose

Date est.
1987

Size/acres
1.5

Residents
5

Visitors
BA, WWOOF

Duartbeg

We have two acres; a narrow strip of land about a quarter of a mile long with the river Jed Water forming the Southern boundary and a 50 foot high cliff to the North. There is a house and workshops one of which used to be a water driven sawmill.

The area we chose for vegetables had been poor pasture. We had this ploughed in the first year and laid out as deep beds cropped on a multiple four course rotation. Between crops the beds are covered with black polythene and the system is easy to operate and productive. A lot of compost is made from grass cuttings etc.

We planted a wide selection of soft fruit which, from past experience, we knew was the most productive thing in the garden with least effort. We also planted tree fruit. We eat our own fruit, fresh, frozen or in jam all the year.

I have kept bees for a long time and now have a productive apiary; seven hives at present.

We burn wood in a stove that heats water and supplies radiators. The house is well insulated.

We have planted alder and willow for coppicing for firewood. We have also planted oak, ash, beech and decorative species. There have been few failures and growth is good.

We have sought to improve the environment for birds and animals. In addition to the planted trees we have left many areas wild, and one area managed as a wild flower meadow; already there are orchids appearing spontaneously. All this has led to a increase in birds; I have identified 37 bird species most of which are here regularly. We have a colony of pipistrelle bats in the roof and hedgehogs, moles, mice, frogs and toads are often seen.

2

Mossburnford Mill

Address
Mossburnford Mill
JEDBURGH
Roxburghshire
TD8 6PJ

Telephone
(08354) 344

Contact
David & Marina Catt

Date est.
1983

Size/acres
2

Residents
2

Visitors
BA

3

Rubha Phoil

Address
Rubha Phoil
Armadail Pier
Ardvasar
Sleat
ISLE OF SKYE
IV45 8RS

Telephone
(04714) 312

Contact
Sandra Masson,
Joanna Jackson

Date est.
1990

Size/acres
15

Residents
4

Visitors
BA

Rubha Phoil is a well wooded peninsula situated near the Armadale ferry terminal on the Sleat peninsula of Skye. This area is known as the 'Garden of Skye' because of its deep peat soils and mild climate. Backed by cliffs, with caves and gulleys, the rocky sea shore and offshore islets provide a haven for seals, sea otters and birds such as herons, Arctic terns and sea eagles. We now have crofting status, and are working closely with Scottish Natural Heritage, the Forestry Authority and Crofters Commission.

The goal is a lush cool temperate rain forest of around forty species of mixed conifer and broadleaves with eventually a whole range of age classes. Shelter will be maintained in perpetuity, with a high rate of carbon assimilation and will produce a sustained yield of timber and fuel. The soil will be continually improved by these new plantings and aided by the use of Jean Pain style composting of brushwood, together with seaweed and bracken, to restore all those nutrients lost over the centuries. Worm breeding and distribution is included in the plan.

The silvicultural system will be a variant on the Bradford-Hutt plan for continuous canopy, irregular forestry, providing a superb habitat for midge consuming birds! Not least as an example of crofting forestry. We are also establishing a native species tree nursery. By creating a nature trail, we hope to promote the Rubha as an educational resource and we aim to offer a wide variety of educational activities. By using natural soil reconditioning methods, we are developing kitchen gardens and forest garden areas, with emphasis on organic varieties adapted to these climatic conditions. Most of the land will remain a wilderness.

After living on the land for some months – simply observing, we are now at the exciting stage of physically working on our Phase one activities, which include: tree planting, ditching, designing buildings, rhododendron removal. In Summer 1993 we will be constructing our multipurpose workshop, built to an approved traditional design. This will free more space in our polytunnel and also provide respite from the heavy rainfall - two metres per year! Bring your wellies!

4

Those his smallholding of 6.5 acres lies at 1050 feet, overlooking the Calder Valley, with a South facing aspect. The family of four adults and two children have lived here for nine years. The land is gradually being transformed from sheep and dairy grazing to trees and perennial crops. Projects so far set up include a shelterbelt of indigenous trees, a paddock for wildlife, watercress in streams, mushrooms on logs, raised beds on a deep-mulch, no-dig system, perennial herbs, vegetables and flowers, water barrels and butts, comfrey and nettle jauches, chicken and geese keeping, microclimate creation for young and tender crops.

Recent projects include investigation into biodynamic gardening methods, creation of biodynamic compost heap and spraying for nutrition and root crops. Future projects include beekeeping and more efficient water recycling. The main necessity however is more efficient use of energy/heat for the farmhouse. We are looking into three possibilities – small wind generator, solar panels and anaerobic digestion, maybe all three if finances allow – any suggestions would be gladly received.

Hebden Bridge

Address
Wicken Hill Farm
Heights Road
HEBDEN BRIDGE
West Yorkshire
HX7 5RF

Telephone
(0422) 885249

Contact
Marilyn Edwards

Date est.
1990

Size/acres
6.5

Residents
6

Visitors
BA

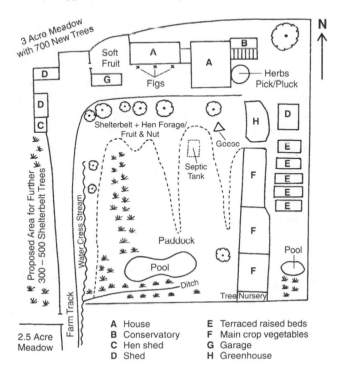

A House
B Conservatory
C Hen shed
D Shed
E Terraced raised beds
F Main crop vegetables
G Garage
H Greenhouse

5

Middle Wood

Address
Middle Wood
Roeburndale West
Wray
LANCASTER
LA2 8QX

Telephone
(05242) 21880

Contact
Rod Everett
Anne Bilbrough

Date est.
1984

Size/acres
235

Residents
3 – 5

Visitors
BA, working
volunteers

Middle Wood is run by a charitable Trust and the farm, woodlands and buildings are being developed as a focus for education and research into techniques which do not cause long term damage to the environment. On site there is a demonstration organic garden which includes specific permacultural techniques such as a chicken tractor and living tree mulch belts. The farm is run organically, stock are treated with homeopathic remedies and we are experimenting with tree based fodder. The woodland of native trees acts as a wonderful learning area for seeing nature at work; part of this is being brought back into coppice production to provide craft materials.

The Study Centre completed in late 1992 has been designed with many permacultural considerations. The building is made from reclaimed timber with a 6 inch frame clad on the outside with waney edge board of elm treated with linseed oil and to the North a stone wall. The main structure from inside to out is plasterboard, 0.5 inch cavity, vapour barrier paper, 6 inches of sheep's wool insulation, breather paper, 0.75 inch cavity then cladding. Sheep's wool insulation contains waterproofing lanolin and is treated with quassia, a tree based moth proofer.

Ceilings and floors are insulated with cork board. On the North side the floor boards are laid directly onto 4 inches of cork and the ceiling is exposed oak board lying over the beams. This produces a well insulated low mass part of the building which can heat up quickly. Light comes through small double glazed k-glass windows.

To the south side 70% of the wall is glazed with k-glass double glazing as a heat collector. This lets in the sun's heat into a central stone wall of 18 inches thick and to a dark coloured floor of 2 inches of concrete over 16 inches of rubble sitting on 4 inches of cork insulation. These two large masses act as a heat store and provide the main heating for the building. Back up heating is provided by bottled gas, which isn't ideal, but more efficient than oil, coal or electric.

Water consumption is reduced by using Humus compost toilets and a small reed bed for dealing with sink and shower water. The toilet compost provides fertility for fruit trees. The roof is made up of 6 inches of cork insulation overlaid with a woodchip and bitumen corrugated material, butyl rubber and 4 inches of earth. Strawberries, bilberries, lawn chamomile, thyme and other low growing herbs provide a final cover. Electricity comes from a 2 kilowatt Proven windmill, a store of 24 volt batteries and a Trace inverter to raise the power to 240 volts.

Middle Wood Trust runs regular Permaculture Design Courses and Permaculture Volunteer Weekends as well as many other 'green' courses. It is also available for hire to like minded groups.

Middle Wood Study Centre showing elm boarding and rear stone cladding. Note small north windows and turf roof.

Middle Wood Study Centre showing south facing glazing of k-glass, dark floor and central wall which act as heat stores.

6

Springfield Community Garden

Address
Stirling Crescent
Holmewood
BRADFORD
BD4

Telephone
(0274) 753924

Contact
Chris Mackenzie Davey

Date est.
1993

Size/acres
7.5

Residents
0
(Site Warden to be appointed)

Visitors
BA,
no accomodation
(at present)

Springfield Community Garden is within the Holmewood Housing Estate in South East Bradford and is a component of the five year programme of improvements to the area. The design has been developed from a brief put together by local people. It includes the following main components:

- The growing of food stuffs, vegetables, fish, poultry and eggs, nuts and berries etc. for local use. Specialised growing of high value cash crops such as garlic, coriander, land and water cress and winter salads is intended.

- Provision of training opportunities for people with learning difficulties.

- Garden design and maintenance education for local people.

- Provision of plants and materials related to edible landscaping to local gardeners.

- Food processing and home economics facilities.

- Open space area to provide recreation and playing space within sight of the kitchen for young people accompanying adults onto the site.

- Provision of workshop spaces for carpentry and green woodwork activities.

The proposed permaculture design seeks to create an abundant and delightful landscape which encourages an air of active sociability around self reliance and healthy eating. The produce will make significant differences to the household economies of participating gardeners and will encourage people to take charge of developing proactive and practical strategies for the relief of poverty.

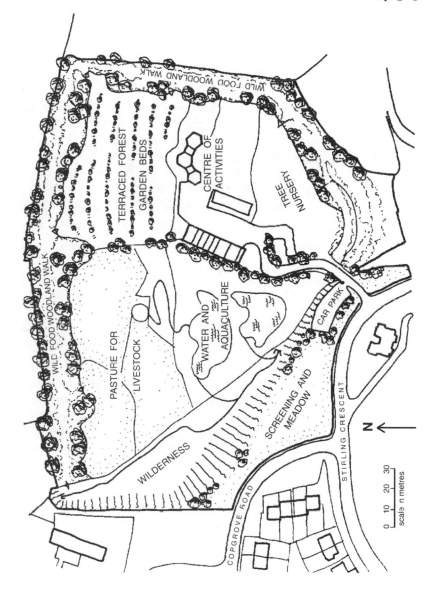

Springfield Community Garden

WILD FOOD WOODLAND WALK

TERRACED FOREST GARDEN BEDS

CENTRE OF ACTIVITIES

TREE NURSERY

WILD FOOD WOODLAND WALK

PASTURE FOR 'LIVESTOCK'

WATER AND AQUACULTURE

CAR PARK

WILDERNESS

SCREENING AND MEADOW

COPGROVE ROAD

STIRLING CRESCENT

N ←

0 10 20 30
scale n metres

29

7

Todmorden

Address
*7 Carr House Fold
TODMORDEN
Lancashire
OL14 8AR*

Telephone
(0706) 818902

Contact
Pam Colbran

Date est.
1990

Size/acres
0.5

Residents
1

Visitors
BA

This is half an acre of hillside which was originally mainly bracken and brambles. The garden is being constructed with an awareness of the usage of the plants in combination with their beauty and colour. The plants are chosen for their medicinal, culinary, visual and general uses. The planting scheme relies on companion planting as well as putting the plant in a site it enjoys.

The hillside is now terraced. The steep section at the top has comfrey filled swales feeding water to the shrubs and trees planted there. A mixed shelterbelt is establishing around the borders of the site with extra broadleaved trees planted on the adjoining hillside. An infant forest garden occupies the middle terrace with an arched covered path linking it to the sitting area at the top. Edible and useful climbers will be trained over the arches with fruit trees interspersed along the edges.

At the other end of the forest garden a pathway leads down bordered by raspberry canes which double as pea canes. On the next level there will be a pond on which we eventually hope to house ducks. At present (beyond the pond site) is a greenhouse and waist high borders to hold 'cut and come again' and 'pick and pluck' plants. On the lowest terrace is another lean-to greenhouse, cold frames, beds for annual vegetables and a border for the perennial shade lovers.

A hazel tunnel has been planted to form a secret approach to the forest garden. Near the house (which is 20 feet below the garden) are several containers growing herbs and plants for culinary use. I am exploring the potential of water turbines, to use the steep gradient of the garden.

Terrace view, 7 Carr House Fold

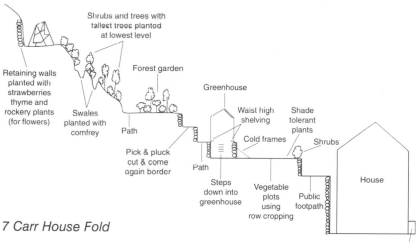

Shrubs and trees with
tallest trees planted
at lowest level

Forest garden

Greenhouse

Retaining walls
planted with
strawberries
thyme and
rockery plants
(for flowers)

Swales
planted with
comfrey

Path

Waist high
shelving

Shade
tolerant
plants

Cold frames

Shrubs

Pick & pluck
cut & come
again border

Path

Steps
down into
greenhouse

Vegetable
plots
using
row cropping

Public
footpath

House

Container grown herbs

7 Carr House Fold

8

Windermere

Address
5 Mill Rise
WINDERMERE
Cumbria
LA23 2LY

Telephone
(05394) 88261

Contact
Debbie Binch

Date est.
1991

Size/acres
0.02

Residents
2

Visitors
BA,
no accommodation

The house and garden form part of a new Council estate. The two small patches of ground at the front were turfed already, with soil depth front and back very shallow. The larger back garden faces north-east with a third overshadowed by an oak tree. The back garden has been constantly mulched. One of the main considerations in the initial design was which route the washing line was to take! The ground is on a slight incline (towards the house) so tree trunks were brought in to make three terraces. A mixed hedge was planted along the back fence, more vertical growing space was provided by making trellises along the side boundaries.

It was soon apparent that slugs – all sizes and colours – were abundant. I decided to grow what they didn't eat. Most fruit and many herbs fit into this category so it works well. The front garden falls away from the house and has been terraced. Mainly fruit again here, but the slugs are not quite as voracious so a few hardy vegetables survive. Plans here are for a trellis and structure to support climbing/hanging plants.

The field at the back (not mine) I count as 'Zone 5'. The oak tree overhanging the back garden has not been a problem; the fruit growing underneath has been very productive. This and other mature oaks are now accompanied by about 250 young mixed natives with an occasional wild pear and damson mixed in. They will provide a habitat for wildlife and local people and be a good wind shield. I am keen to make further links both between the house and garden, and between No. 5 and the people living nearby. My aim with the garden is to make maximum use of a relatively small piece of land.

A shram Acres is an organic land use project in inner city Birmingham. It was started by local residents (including members of an intentional community who had been living in the neighbourhood for the past 5 years) as a response to wasted skills and wasted land in Sparkbrook, a region of high unemployment and multiple deprivation. Five Victorian gardens were cleared of rubbish to create over 0.5 acre of intensively cultivated land. A high proportion of the local population is of Asian or Afro-Caribbean origin, and Ashram Acres specialises in growing Asian and Caribbean plants, such as karella, aubergine and chilli, in two polytunnels on site. The project is almost entirely self-financing and up to 1988 was run by volunteers only. There are 20 members from a range of backgrounds contributing £2.70 a week, receiving vegetables in return, and volunteering at regular Saturday work-ins. In addition, vegetables are sold to local people who visit the garden and at seasonal stalls in the area. Ashram Acres also keeps two goats, quail, rabbits, ducks and bees. Children can join in activities at regular opening times in the evenings.

Ashram Acres has been organic since its inception and tries to incorporate sustainability in all areas of planning. Inner city refuse, normally discarded, has been put to good use in a number of ways. Ashram Acres has also featured in studies and television programmes on environmental initiatives in the city.

Volunteers interested in working in either of these projects can come through WWOOF, but also through personal arrangements for various lengths of time. In both cases, please write or phone in advance.

9

Ashram Acres

Address
Ashram Acres
23-25 Grantham Road
Sparkbrook
BIRMINGHAM
B11 1LU

Telephone
021-773 7061

Contact
Ute Jaeckel

Date est.
1981

Size/acres
0.5

Residents
5 – 20

Visitors
BA, WWOOF

10

Camphill Water

Address
Camphill Water
Oaklands Park
NEWNHAM
Gloucestershire
GL14 1EF

Telephone
(0594) 516063

Contact
Mark Moodie

Date est.
1985

Size/acres
160

Residents
90

Visitors
BA, 1st Monday
of each month
at 3pm

The sewage systems at Oaklands Park and others built along the same lines are compatible with many of permaculture's ethics. What makes it all the more interesting is that the ideas were developed by NASA and the Max-Planck Institute. However, a more expected bedfellow, biodynamics within Camphill Communities, has developed the idea to make it practical, reliable, beautiful and practically odourless. Oaklands Park gave Uwe Burka a mandate to correct the sewage systems since they were discharging above their consent. Water authorities eventually gave their blessing for a system in Uwe's garden but not without reluctance: sewage treatment has mainly been mechanical or chemical in recent years. The idea that a garden full of plants might do the job all year round as well or better was an about turn to be taken only after much thought.

The first system was a series of four terraces set into the landscape. Each terrace held sand and stones to a depth of 40cm. Growing in this medium are reeds, bulrushes, iris and sedges. The sewage solids are settled and the liquid effluent is distributed over the surface of the first terrace and moves vertically through the bed. The liquid coats each grain and pebble in a thin layer, while the gaps between the stones contain oxygen to feed the microorganisms that detoxify the liquid. Oxygen is replenished by the plants' roots. The final effluent is of EC bathing water quality.

However, the organic load that entered is still present in the water, better called nutrients. In the systems currently being designed, withy beds are created to receive this irrigation. In the biodynamic philosophy it is advised not to use this to grow human food. To extend the cycle between human shit and human food is considered important, but to grow trees that also clean the air is fine.

The success of the first system has led Uwe to build another at Oaklands Park for 100 people. There is now a company, Camphill Water, to design and build these systems for others willing to take on the challenges of looking after a system. The skills are those of a caring gardener rather than an engineer – cutting the plants once a year and changing the flow from one part of the first terrace to another every so often to allow the former to dry out – to remineralise.

Reed bed system, Camphill Water

11

Centre for Alternative Technology

Address
*Centre for
Alternative
Technology
Llwyngwern Quarry
MACHYNLLETH
Powys
SY2 9AZ*

Telephone
(0654) 702400

Contact
Peter Harper

Date est.
1974

Size/acres
40

Residents
15

Visitors
*BA, working
volunteers*

The Centre for Alternative Technology began with a group of people determined to prove that it is possible to live lightly on the earth, replenishing and recycling whatever they take from its resources so that it can be a sustainable way of life, that leaves the planetary systems unchanged for future generations.

This objective has been developed by the Community living here since 1974 and the Centre has always been open to the general public so that they can visit and see different ways in which they can adapt their lives and their homes to this effect.

Using renewable energy as much as possible, sharing this energy and adapting buildings to save energy; growing vegetables and fruit without chemicals harmful to the soil; recycling and composting waste so nothing is lost from the system; working together as equals and sharing out the mundane, routine jobs; buying food, cooking and eating together and looking after the animals; all these things are incorporated into the life of the Community.

Recent developments at the Centre include experiments with reed bed sewage systems, which could be important in saving the world's water resources and a water-balanced cliff railway supplied from a new lake, showing the use of renewable energy to carry people up steep slopes.

Children and educational groups are encouraged to spend time at the Centre and can arrange to stay for several days in cabins which are designed to be self-sufficient so that they have the opportunity to see how the future of the planet could be managed.

The Centre also runs residential courses each year on wind, water and solar energy systems, organic growing and permaculture, self-build and blacksmithing. This is all part of the Centre's commitment to spreading as much information about these subjects to as many people as possible.

Eco-cabins showing turf roofs, Centre for Alternative Technology

Reed bed system for eco-cabins, Centre for Alternative Technology

12

Earthworm

Address
*Earthworm
Housing Co-op
Wheatstone
Leintwardine
CRAVEN ARMS
Shropshire
SY7 0LH*

Telephone
(05473) 461

Contact
*Hil, Tiny, Emma,
Laura, Viv, Bar*

Date est.
1989

Size/acres
7

Residents
13

Visitors
BA, WWOOF

We began in late 1989 with 7 acres, a large house and former stable. The buildings were totally vandalised and are still largely in disrepair. The design of the house (1909) affords neither easy maintenance nor ecological efficiency.

We ceased using the flush toilet in 1991 due to the septic tank being overfull, obsolete and condemned. We built the first compost toilet vault in 1991 and added three in 1992. The vaults are built of brick and breeze block with concrete floor and render, loosely based on a Vietnamese design. Recently Bay No 1 was closed down after a year of use. Comfrey is planted all round the site to soak up any seepage. Smell and flies are rarely a problem so long as strict hygiene is kept.

Only 3 of the 7 acres are regularly worked. In 1991 we adopted a more permaculture approach after hosting a Design Course. We moved the main vegetable garden from the furthest field to outside the back door and started to grow more perennial crops. We're planting dwarf fruit trees, soft fruit and companion flowers and herbs. Perennials are stocked in a herb spiral and in borders and pots around the house. We mulch extensively with straw, cardboard (4.5 tons so far) and old carpet.

On the perimeter of our camping field we have started three crescent shaped mini forest gardens. Comfrey root cuttings were used as an edge, fruit and nut trees were planted through mulch behind soft fruit and perennial herbs. Baby oak, sweet chestnut, ash and hazel have been added behind and between the crescents and along all the perimeters.

Our communal diet is predominantly vegan so our gardening methods are too. We don't keep food animals, so effective recycling of human wastes will be important to maintain fertility. The community is run as a co-operative, responsibilities and decision-making shared by all. We are part of Radical Routes, a national network of co-ops who are funded via our own ethical investment loan stock scheme and who operate skills and resource exchanges.

The plot is rectangular, 1.25 acres, flat, with a stream along the north-east boundary with associated trees and thick tall hedge next to the bridle way along the northwest boundary. It can flood in winter but has land drains. There is a tendency to late spring frosts.

Five years ago it was mainly down to grass. It now has an establishing forest zone – a mix of oak, ash, cherry, hazel, hornbeam, alder – a shelterbelt/fuelwood coppice, a horseshoe shaped orchard/embryonic forest garden enclosing a South facing area of raised vegetable beds, a hazel area for nuts and a wild meadow and pond.

The forest trees have put on very good growth this year (1992). There was the first acorn and the first hazel nut. Fruit tree planting is finished for the time being while I add to the shrubs and bushes – blackcurrant and gooseberry. I'm also adding to the climbers. Continental walnut varieties have finally looked alive.

The willow coppice is still being extended. A tolerant neighbour has enabled me to solve the problem of blocked land drains creatively and I'm digging a series of drainage ditches to replace drains through the willow area. I'm beginning to see the possibility of aquaculture sometime in the future. It will be interesting to see if having more water around in ditches will reduce the frost risk (warming the air, draining away cold air?).

Fertility is improving quite quickly due to closed loops for sewage (all mine ends up on the land eventually) and wood ash. Essex red clover provides a lot of mulch, cut several times a year. Meadow provides hay mulch for the forest garden. Wild species of plant and animals are thriving – about 15 species of butterfly, grass snakes, frogs, toads, hare, two types of orchid. All from land that was down to market gardening a decade or so ago. No rabbits yet and the birds only took the first week's crop of raspberries.

13

Evesham

Address
c/o 1 Merstow
Cottages
Merstow Place
EVESHAM
Worcestershire
WR11 4AY

Telephone
(0386) 48448

Contact
John Porter

Date est.
1987

Size/acres
1.25

Residents
none

Visitors
BA

14

Fairacre (Erw Dêg)

Address
Fairacre (Erw Dêg)
Cwm Cych
NEWCASTLE
EMLYN
Dyfed
SA38 9RR

Telephone
(0239) 77370

Contact
Tony Wrench,
Jane Faith

Date est.
1990

Size/acres
1.5

Residents
4

Visitors
BA

O ur bungalow in a field is gradually disappearing as wood store, solar shower, conservatory and scullery have sprouted from it while the surrounding vegetation gets taller and more dense. We now have a fairly extensive rainwater harvesting system and have installed a wind generator and solar panels to run the lights, which are now on 12 volts. Making much use of second-hand glass from local glazier. Use a lot of mulches in the garden. Black plastic good for spuds and leeks. New deep hay bed brilliant for spinach. Wildlife on the increase. We're still working out the balance between slugs, ducks, cats, fox, toads and chickens. It seems to hinge on movable 4-foot fences, frog corridors (oh yes) and vigilance. We're learning Welsh. Visitors are especially welcome when they bring a boot full of plants for exchange. We are now much happier with the south end of the house, which looks like this:

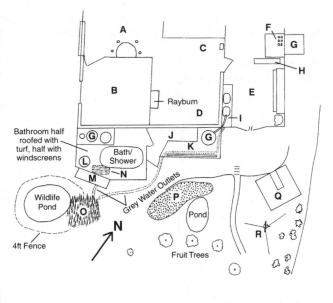

A Eating area	**J** Glass roofed conservatory
B Study	**K** Bed for exotics (guava etc.)
C Cooking area	**L** Solar hot tank
D Sitting area	**M** Solar water panel
E Scullery	**N** Grey water
F 12v battery bank & fuses	**O** Reeds
G Water storage	**P** Vegetables
H Photovoltaic cells on roof	**Q** Windscreen greenhouse
I Rainwater feed to sink	**R** Rutland wind generator

T he First World War brought the farming community a false prosperity with a large increase
in the use of fertilisers to produce extra food at
home. A reduction in the animal population and the
vast increase in fertilisers started a downward trend in
soil fertility. When hard times came in the 1920s and
30s, there were financial difficulties with fertiliser firms;
then a gradual restriction in everything that aided soil
fertility. In these sandy, sloping fields, which were bare
during the winter, soil bacteria soon began to die away.
The slopes became thinner and sandier and the best soil
was washed to the bottom of the field. All this broke
Father's health and he died when I was only 14. Taking
on a run down farm at this age, seemed very enormous
for me; but the alternative was even worse. I was
convinced I could restore the old fertility.

The rotation that has gradually developed achieves
a complete coverage of all the field and provides
adequate food for all the year round open air feeding
for over 100 cattle and 100 sheep lambs; it has slowly
eliminated all corn growing, cash root crops and root
crops for our cattle. Our rotation is achieved by carefully
resting and rotating our field pastures to produce winter
grazing on a 3 year cycle. The mixture used for these
pastures includes rye-grass, cocksfoot, timothy, fescue,
clover, chicory, sheep's parsley, kidney vetch, yarrow
and nettle. November to December grazing is achieved
by resting 50 acres from mid-August; January to early
February grazing by resting 50 acres from the end of
August, which is fertilised with all farmyard manures
available and, if necessary, some organic fertilisers.
Seed is cast onto flattened molehills and spread around
by the animals, through their manure or on their claws.
Each field received one of these winter grazings every
3 years. We eliminated the need to return any fields to
a root break for autumn and spring grazing.

The advantages with our grass rotation system are
that the fields are never bare. These rotations help to
eliminate plant and animal diseases. We think the battle
for good health both in plant and animal is fought in
the top two inches of soil with the larger animals and
micro-organisms. The whole area in the early autumn
and spring is one vast turmoil with an up and down
battle going on between all sizes and types of animals,

15

Fordhall
Farm

Address
*Fordhall Farm
MARKET
DRAYTON
Shropshire
TF9 3PR*

Telephone
(0630) 638255

Contact
Arthur Hollins

Date est.
1946

Size/acres
150

Residents
1

Visitors
BA

bacteria, fungi and micro-organisms, the farmer using balanced rotations to nurse and study these cycles that go on in the soil.

We have spent 15 years studying a 1/8 acre plot that was laid down to study what happens when our farming system of permanent cover is compared with a plot where seed is sown on sterile sand and shale. The plot had all the soil removed, then seeded with all kind of grasses, herbs, sand-dune grasses and weeds and then covered with one-inch square nylon mesh. It took about 7 years for most of the seed to germinate – the sand dune grasses germinated first and provided the necessary cover. No manures were added, it was left entirely to nature. Most of the grasses are now fully established and the soil insects are there in normal numbers, followed by moles. The most exciting result is that 2.5 inches of good quality loamy soil and roots is now established on top of the nylon mesh, in only 18 years.

Under the foggage system the amount of soil that has come all over my farm must be even greater. Modern systems of cultivation create a similar result but in the other direction; 2.5 inches is lost forever and brings in the need to feed the land, even organic arable land. This also accounts for the plants on our farm always having their main new roots on the surface under the leaf cover; they are following the area of chemical synthesis within the top inch under the protective cover of the plants returning leaf fall, which is occurring all year round. The importance of this cannot be over estimated. We are seeing the reality of soil production instead of steady permanent soil erosion; the insects do it for us.

We are now in the process of developing a machine we've called 'the Culturseeder' so that permanent cover can be achieved with all arable land anywhere in the world, crops can be grown in a real sustainable system with a steady rise in fertility, cutting completely the need for fertilisers, lime, pesticides etc.

As farmers, we can only guess at what really goes on and judge from what appears to bring results, balancing the needs of all our plants and animals with the elements, assisting nature in her struggle to produce a surplus and using that surplus for raising our standard of living.

The house is designed to be largely run on home-produced timber. It incorporates a Kachel-oven for background heat and other stoves for water. Drainage is separated to black and grey water – the former goes to a bark pit for composting, the latter out into the fields, possibly later into willow coppice. The main building was completed by March 1993.

The land is mainly wetland and degraded grazing occupied by ducks and a shire horse and foal. Much tree planting is envisioned for shelter, fuel and commercial purposes. Old waterways abound and will be integrated into a swale/aquaculture system when I have a) the time, money and equipment and b) the faintest inkling of what to do.

Vegetable garden, fruit trees and all those design-sexy items have yet to appear beyond my fevered imagination. People with motivation to act in these areas will receive particularly large portions of teacake.

There is a caravan for visitors to stay in and for students of archaeology to examine. Plenty of camping space, tools and scope for action-hungry types. We do not smoke, we do not eat meat, have a baby, disagree violently over the Archers and abhor political correctness.

16

Gelli Ddewi Isaf

Address
Gelli Ddewi Isaf
Parc y Rhos
Cwm-Ann
LAMPETER
Dyfed
SA48 8EA

Telephone
(0570) 423065

Contact
Ali Kaye,
Nathaniel Holt

Date est.
1991

Size/acres
30

Residents
3

Visitors
BA

17

Highwood Hill

Address
Highwood Hill
Rushbury
CHURCH
STRETTON
Shropshire
SY6 7DE

Telephone
(0694) 771342

Contact
Robert Hart

Date est.
1985

Size/acres
1

Residents
1

Visitors
BA

The primary aim of the Forest Garden scheme on Wenlock Edge is to demonstrate a system which would enable a family or community to achieve a degree of self-sufficiency in food, herbs and small timber throughout the year. While the forest garden areas, comprising shade-tolerant fruit, nut, herb and perennial vegetable plants, constitute the heart of the system, other areas are designed to utilise the full potentialities of the site:

1. Open areas, for sun-loving vegetables and herbs.
2. Wetland areas, for plants that grow in water or bogs, including a reedbed system for purifying effluent.
3. Container areas, for plants in tubs, e.g. 'patio garden', 'bedsit garden'.
4. Big tree area, for trees that will grow too large for a forest garden.
5. Willow coppices, cut for basketry, shredded for compost.
6. Small greenhouse.

As far as possible, the whole scheme complies with three 'forest principles':

- The soil is kept permanently mulched with organic hay, straw, grass cuttings or compost and is undisturbed.
- Multiple cropping is practised in all areas.
- Aromatic plants are grown to purify the atmosphere and ward off pests and diseases.

The scheme also includes a small Ecological House with wood-burning stove, organic loo and wind generator for lighting. See *Forest Gardening* by Robert A. de J. Hart, Green Books 1991 (available from Permanent Publications).

In 1992 the Forest Garden received more than 450 visitors from 26 countries, many of them drawn by the article in *The Permaculture Plot*. Most of them expressed keen interest and many expressed a desire to establish similar schemes. I regard the Forest Garden as a link between the international permaculture movement and the international Agroforestry movement, whose headquarters are the International Centre for Research in

Agroforestry (ICRAF), Nairobi, Kenya. I would much like to see close liaison between the two movements, in particular 'twinning' between permaculture groups and forest garden communities in tropical areas.

Above:
Forest Garden,
Highwood Hill

Left:
Robert Hart,
Forest Garden
pioneer

Primrose Farm

Address
Primrose Farm
Felindre
BRECON
Powys
LD3 0ST

Telephone
(0497) 847636

Contact
Paul Benham

Date est.
1988

Size/acres
6

Residents
2 – 3

Visitors
BA, WWOOF

Primrose Farm is an ecological smallholding of 6 acres. 3/4 acre consists of a highly productive organic market garden producing most of the holding's income, which is sufficient for mortgage, bills, living and slow improvements. 30-40 different vegetables and 60-70 varieties of herb plants with beneficial uses are often available and everything is sold locally. The high diversity produces a more balanced system less vulnerable to growing and marketing problems. An enormous amount is produced from a small area. However this is achieved at present with a very large labour input. Since the income from this area is so essential, transition to permaculture principles must come slowly. However this year some organic mulching will be done.

Productive trees are being encouraged on the holding and now 69 different varieties of fruit and nut trees are planted. 44 of these are within the 1/3 acre forest garden which is similar to that designed by Robert Hart. At present there are 3 central areas in which annual vegetables are grown. A large asparagus bed has been introduced in a section along the south side and from there the canopy rises through rhubarb and Jerusalem artichokes, tayberries and grapevines, to bush fruit trees, to half standards and nut trees near the hedge on the north side.

Tayberries, Japanese wineberries, grapevines and raspberries provide the climbing layer. Jostaberries, Worcesterberries, gooseberries and red, black and white currants are the bush fruit layer. 8 varieties of mints, lovage, sorrel, nasturtiums and many different squashes make up the ground layer. This year the floor of the forest garden was mulched with waste threshed rye grass. The area is considered to play an important role in the future of the holding and ideas developed there will be incorporated into the management of the market garden.

On 4.5 acres grassland range a cow and calf, 2 goats, 15 ewes, bees and soon ducks. The animals produce some income, consume garden waste and provide manure and interest value. The ducks will have restricted access to the garden to combat the desperate slug problem. A large pond is being dug for the ducks and two smaller ones to encourage frogs. Turf from the pond area will provide roofing for a new shed.

Whe have a 60 acre mixed stock farm, mainly under grass at present. Our aim is to find ways of making traditional grassland systems more sustainable. We are also slowly taking land out of grassland to be put to more productive uses.

Things to see and work to do!

- Direct marketing of meat with customer involvement in the farm.
- Working towards self-sufficiency in animal feed especially with comfrey for pigs.
- Kachelofen built by Reinhart von Zchock.
- Artist blacksmith's forge
- Setting up 1 acre vegetable Community Supported Agriculture (CSA) project and two polytunnels
- 3 acre new chestnut plantation
- Half acre fish pond with chinampas – vegetable beds combined with aquaculture systems
- Farm used as site for residential courses
- Coppicing
- DIY solar panels/solar house design

Most projects are in their early stages so we can't claim to be demonstrating anything spectacular.

19

Ragmans Lane Farm

Address
Ragmans Lane Farm
Lower Lydbrook
LYDBROOK
Gloucestershire
GL17 9PA

Telephone
(0594) 860244

Contact
Matt Dunwell,
Jan Davies

Date est.
1990

Size/acres
60

Residents
5

Visitors
BA, WWOOF

Comfrey planting for pig forage,
Ragmans Lane Farm

20

Rose
Garth

Address
Rose Garth
Storridge
MALVERN
Worcestershire
WR13 5EL

Telephone
(0886) 880849

Contact
Paul & Jeanne
Millsom

Date est.
1989

Size/acres
5.5

Residents
5

Visitors
BA

The plot is generally southeast facing on a steep slope with a yellow clay subsoil, but sunlight exposure is reduced by the high tree covered hill opposite. The house (c.1840) is situated on the lowest corner of the land, by a major road. No permaculturist would build a home here considering the reduced sunlight, car pollution and poor scope for aquaculture, but the original occupants were interested in roadside custom. A good stand of established oak and birch lines the top third of the land.

Our first three years were the dry hot summers and so the few trees that were planted had to be tended well. Brambles emerged almost everywhere and these have proved to be a great asset. The masses of blackberries are utilised and the foliage provides perfect conditions for natural regeneration and tree shelter. Even an apple has seeded in the protection of the bramble.

Planting started in earnest in the winter of 1991/2 and now exceeds 1000 trees. The land is now surrounded by woodland (wild cherry, wild pear, wild service, chestnut, hazel, whitebeam and oak). A conspicuous forest garden (1/4 acre) is noticed from the road. A less densely planted rear garden has beds for annuals and space for chickens. In the centre of the woodland is a densely planted orchard with over 30 varieties of apple, plus pears, plums, damsons, cherries, pea trees, 'sweet' oaks, chestnuts, cobnuts and mulberries.

An arboretum boasts butternuts, walnuts, strawberry tree, hackberry, raisin tree, Russian olive, persimmon and honey locust.

Energy self-sufficiency is a challenge considering the age and situation of the house, which is mainly heated by wood from the plot.

Next year we will supply the local organic grocer's shop. The produce will be clearly described as 'Permaculture Grown' with leaflets that provide a brief definition. What better way to publicise permaculture?

My permaculture plot proceeds slowly since becoming inspired by Robert Hart's forest garden on the television programme, Muck 'n' Magic. I made a start with fruit and then attended a Forest Garden Design Course, which confirmed my direction. My fruit is all young and I can't visualise expected yield on maturity – or when maturity will come.

In my 0.05 acre I have 12 apple trees totalling 24 varieties plus 2 minarette pear, 3 blackberry, 3 raspberry, 4 blueberry, 4 blackcurrant, gooseberry, cherry, outdoor grape, loganberry, veitchberry, boysenberry and several strawberries. Great for a munching walk but not enough for bowls full. I can't imagine being self-sufficient in fruit – it must take acres. My sycamores may cast too much shade for what I'm trying to do but the blackcurrants and Malling Admiral seem successful.

For 10 days in 1991 I kept some chickens on the ark system but a local dog proved my feeling that arks are 'sitting ducks' and a friend euthanased them. I am part way through building a roofed-in lean-to verandah which will keep my washing dry, support and protect my grape and provide a Fort Knox electric-fenced straw yard habitat.

Another addition in May 1992 was a greenhouse, on the premise that cloches do much for plants and nothing for gardeners. In the first months it was too hot, in Autumn it was too damp and at Christmas all my winter salad drooped during the hard frosts. I'm not sure I've got the hang of it yet. Highlight of 1992 – metaldehyde going back on the organic list – maybe it will be worth trying to grow salads outside.

21

Solihull

Address
14 Hanson Grove
SOLIHULL
West Midlands
B92 7QB

Telephone

Contact
Laura Englefield

Date est.
1989

Size/acres
0.05

Residents
1

Visitors
BA,
no accommodation

22

Tai
Madog

Address
3 Tai Madog
Stablau
Llanrug
CAERNARFON
Gwynedd
LL55 3PH

Telephone
(0286) 870606

Contact
Jill Jackson,
Owen Smith

Date est.
1988

Size/acres
3

Residents
2

Visitors
BA

We live in a terraced house and have been developing the land on the hillside directly behind us along permaculture principles. The land is rocky and poor having formerly been rough grazing for sheep and horses. On the relatively flat ground nearest the house we have an area of approximately 25 raised beds where we grow a wide selection of vegetables organically using lots of mulches, which is sufficient to feed ourselves for most of the year. We are particularly interested in growing unusual food crops – both annual and perennial, as a means of diversification. We also have a polytunnel where we grow a number of less hardy crops such as peppers and tomatoes along with perennials such as kiwi fruit and grape vines. We use several of the raised beds for the production of seeds and tubers of unusual vegetables and fruits. These are offered for sale in our mail order catalogue, Future Foods. Send 3 x 1st class stamps for a copy.

The propagation of plants takes place in 'The Pit', a dry-stone walled, polythene clad small greenhouse dug into the ground as an attempt to maintain a more even temperature. In association with the raised bed area are shelterbelts of native tree species and several ponds. We have planted two areas of orchards/forest gardens where we have a variety of common and unusual fruit and nut trees, along with fruit bushes, herbs, perennial vegetables and clovers. We have 4 hives of bees in the lower orchard adjacent to an area of semi-mature oak trees.

Next to the upper orchard are several terraced beds for fruit and vegetable growing and several plots where we are attempting to grow grains using no-till Fukuoka type methods. The highest part of the land, furthest from the house has been planted up with over 1000 native trees – hopefully giving us a wood supply in the long term as well as helping to reforest an area much subject to the overgrazing of sheep.

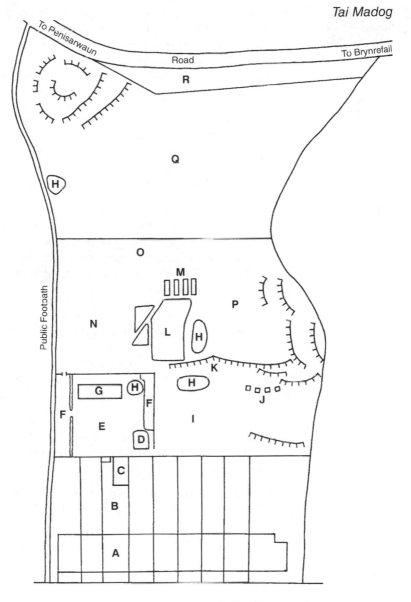

Tai Madog

A House
B Kitchen Garden
C Greenhouse
D 'The Pit'
E Raised beds for vegetables
& seed production
F Shelterbelt
G Polytunnel
H Pond
I Orchard/Forest Garden

J Bee hives
K Climbing fruit up rocks
L No-dig grain/tuber plot
M Terrace beds
N Mixed Orchard
O Walnuts & other nut trees
P Mixed Orchard including
   unusual fruit and nuts
Q Native trees
R Tuber growing area

23

Tir Penhros Isaf

Address
Tir Penrhos Isaf
Hermon
Llanfachreth
DOLGELLAU
Gwynedd
LL40 2LL

Telephone
(0341) 40256

Contact
Lyn, Chris &
Sam Dixon

Date est.
1985

Size/acres
7

Residents
3

Visitors
BA,
no accommodation
Jul – Nov

I was raised in the countryside and my knowledge of flora and fauna comes from hours of sitting in hedge bottoms and tree tops, observing and dreaming. Now I needed somewhere to keep my pony, somewhere I could care for a rich ragwort free pasture, fence off trees, plant hedges and hang gates that opened and closed.

So we searched and at last we found and finally bought our own piece of land. The pasture was old but over-grazed; the marshes were poached mud patches, rails were nailed to oaks, coppice trees nibbled back to desperately budding stumps.

Penniless after our acquisition, we were in no position to instantly transform our land. This was a blessing in disguise. As we passed through the first year, we learnt from the land and it taught us well. We watched and we learned and still we learn, and the more we learn, the more we realise how little we know.

As we observed and interacted with our teacher, there seemed to be a pattern emerging. Sometimes it was confused and blurred, sometimes clear and shining. No longer did we try to impose our ideas and forms on the land, but rather looked at what was there and looked for the mutual benefit for both us and the land.

The land was our orchestra, with talented and various musicians. We the conductor leading it in rhythm and harmony. And oh what a tune she plays when the conductor gets it right.

And of course we weren't the first or last to do this and when we heard of permaculture it crystallised and centred our ethic. Now we have other conductors to share notes with and learn with, and learn with, and learn with, and learn with, and learn with.

And the pony? He's gardening well, Bill.

• Chris Dixon's design for Tir Penrhos Isaf was featured in full in *Permaculture Magazine* Vol. 1 No. 2. *Ed.*

Tir Penrhos Isaf

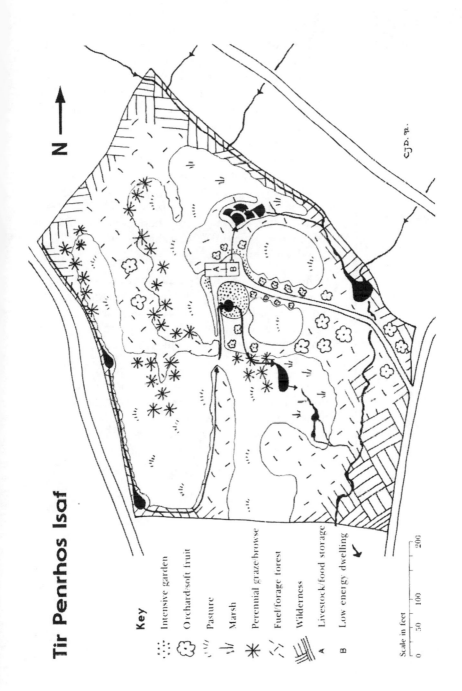

N →

Key

⋮⋮⋮ Intensive garden

🌳 Orchard/soft fruit

ᵛ⁄ᵛ Pasture

⫽ Marsh

✳ Perennial graze/browse

⁄⁄ Fuel/forage forest

▤ Wilderness

A Livestock/food storage

B Low energy dwelling

↘

Scale in feet

0   50   100   200

24

Tyn-y-Fron

Address
Tyn-y-Fron
Maengwynedd
Llanrhaeadr Y.M.
OSWESTRY
Shropshire
SY10 0DE

Telephone
(0691) 780540

Contact
Pen Strange

Date est.
1983

Size/acres
6

Residents
4

Visitors
No thanks

About four of our six acres were planted with native tree species in 1984: that leaves two paddocks where we graze a pony, a young orchard (just beginning to crop well if we get pest control right) and a large garden. Our original design was basically sound, but a) if I'd known more about fencing, there would be more straight lines and right angles in the way the land is divided; and b) the garden we first attempted was too big. We planned to earn money selling organic vegetables, but we now earn money working away from home, so only need enough garden to keep us in vegetables and look good. Our big polythene tunnel has many uses: early spring crops, cucumbers etc. in summer, late salads, drying onions etc. and winter storage (e.g. hay). We keep a few ducks and chickens and have three ponds.

The attached greenhouse all along the south side of the house is a real asset, warming the house quickly from any sun, keeping winds off, providing space for overwintering plants, starting seeds and cuttings, growing tomatoes and leaving wet wellies and coats.

We have no mains services. Our water comes from a spring pumped by a hydraulic ram. There is an outside toilet with a bucket that gets emptied round the fruit trees and bushes, but we are planning an inside toilet soon. Two woodstoves heat the house. After a long wait, we are now in the process of planning and installing a wind generator system to replace an old diesel generator.

Y Felin has been by-passed by the agricultural revolution that has turned farming into an industrial process that maximises production in quantity at the expense of quality, environmental diversity and sustainability.

Situated in a small valley, Y Felin is bordered on the one side by the River Crewi and on the other by oak woods. Over the river is the bracken covered hillside of the Common, a fascinating area of ancient tracks, springs, boggy places and on which the trees and shrubs are making a come back amongst the bracken and gorse. Y Felin land is a mix of hill and riverside meadows with a small mixed wood and hedges that are overgrown. The meadows, long uncultivated and not 'improved', are wonderfully rich in herbs, flowers, fungi and wildlife.

We see our role, as stewards of this land, to work with it not only to support ourselves but also to support the many other plants and creatures with whom we share it. And indeed to encourage an even greater number of species to come and be at home here.

Our initial plans are to:
* preserve the species richness of the meadows.
* regenerate the gardens and orchard.
* start a nursery for native trees from local stock for woodland planting.
* start a nursery for endangered/unusual food plants.
* establish an apiary.
* dig a fish pond and also a wildlife pond.
* renovate the cottage.
* eventually, restore the old chapel as a bunkhouse

In the longer term we envisage running permaculture courses and meetings for the celebration of life and nature.

Our vision is of a smallholding that demonstrates the practicality of permaculture in realising the productive potential of a site whilst enhancing its value as a wildlife habitat. Offers of help would be appreciated.

Y Felin

Address
Y Felin
Melinbyrhedyn
MACHYNLLETH
Powys
SY20 8SH

Telephone
(0654) 702718

Contact
Liza & Tom
Brown

Date est.
1992

Size/acres
7

Residents
2

Visitors
BA

Y Felin

56

T he Dot Hill Forest Garden is a London Wildlife Trust (LWT) Nature Site. It is managed by local people and members of the South East London Permaculture Group (SELP), who have an informal agreement with LWT. It is ex-allotment land, adjacent to active allotments, a park and a housing estate. Natural succession from open cultivated land into woodland has created an interesting mosaic of plant communities. This forms the basis of the forest garden with many fruiting trees and shrubs: apples, pears, damsons, crabs, hips, haws, elder, raspberries, blackberries, currants, gooseberries and grapes. Other useful plants include hops, horseradish, burdock, dandelion, nettle, plantain, cleavers and comfrey. This forest garden has established itself through neglect!

As the site is essentially a nature conservation area there have been few introductions, particularly of alien species. However, in order to increase yield and quality of fruit, pruning and other seasonal management is carried out by SELP. We are looking forward to some good crops although local kids prefer using unripe fruit as missiles and then refreshing themselves with expensive sweets. We are running courses on forest gardening using the site as an example and are trying to involve people living nearby in our activities; so far we have seen a lot of net curtain twitching but little else.

Urban permaculture has some very challenging aspects, with many open spaces being vulnerable to the forces of entropy (vandals, developers, politicians etc.) and require a subtle design approach to create inconspicuous, resilient and productive growing areas. The Dot Hill site is a good example of this and should continue to thrive as a wildlife and community resource.

The site is owned by the London Borough of Greenwich Leisure Services and held under license by the London Wildlife Trust. Access is open, so the site can be visited freely. It is located on Dot Hill Road, Plumstead, London, SE18. Shrewsbury Park is on opposite side of road. Site is 0.5 mile South of Plumstead Common. Pedestrian access is from Dot Hill Road, an unmade road suitable for motor vehicles, between Garland Road and Plum Lane. Grid reference TQ 443 773 (OS 1:50,000 sheet 270).

26

Dot Hill

Address
c/o 7 Elmdene Road
Plumstead
LONDON
SE18 6TZ

Telephone
081-317 8013

Contact
Matthew Rowland

Date est.
1992

Size/acres
1.2

Residents
None

Visitors
Anytime

27

Hatfield

Address
*6 Nash Close
Welham Green
HATFIELD
Hertfordshire
AL9 7NN*

Telephone
(0707) 276754

Contact
*Michael & Julia
Guerra*

Date est.
1991

Size/acres
0.015

Residents
2

Visitors
BA

W e live in a new-built ground floor flat with garden on three sides. So far we have not started on converting the front lawn to productiveness, but 1993 should see that changed. In our small rear and side areas we have managed to grow about 30 varieties of fruit, over 60 herbs, almost 20 sallets and about 50 other different vegetables. We try to ensure constant ground cover especially around the fruit trees and herb beds. We also grow a number of perennial and annual pollen plants amongst all the beds and have a small pond with frogs. Slugs are still a slight problem and we have to resort to the manual method, but as we grow everything within 10m of our back or front door this is not a problem.

Our raised beds are made of old railway sleepers and the paths are the remnants of the patio that covered the whole back area. The beds were filled with a mixture of composts and manures with some sharp sand, as under the paving is consolidated sand with cement on top of heavy clay. We are new gardeners and are learning fast. Even so we manage to keep our food bill down to around £3 each week for 6 months without starving, which is just as well because we are both unwaged.

We would like to experiment with growing a few grains: amaranth, quinoa or oats etc. But most of all we would also like to grow more perennial vegetables. We only spend about 2 hours a week doing any work (not including construction projects – which only amount to a morning at any time). It is a shame that we will probably not be staying here much longer, but we have plans to reproduce – and we could use a little more room!

- Michael and Julia Guerra's design for 6 Nash Close was featured in full in *Permaculture Magazine* Vol. 1 No. 3.
- Following a feature on BBC TV's Gardeners' World on 6th August 1993, the Permaculture Association received over 3,000 enquiries.
  Ed.

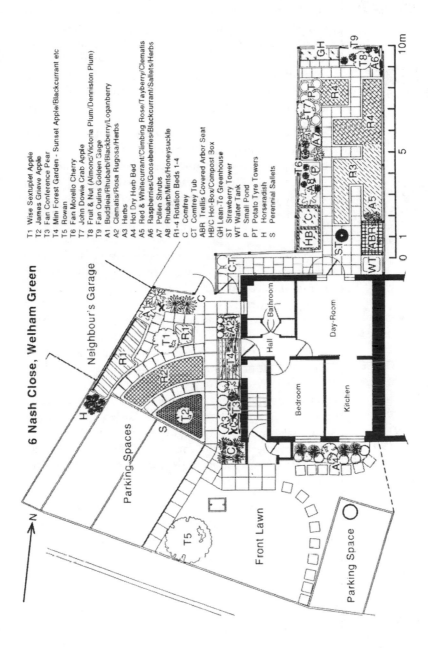

6 Nash Close, Welham Green

T1 Wise Sextuplet Apple
T2 James Grieve Apple
T3 Fan Conference Pear
T4 Mini Forest Garden - Sunset Apple/Blackcurrant etc
T5 Rowan
T6 Fan Morello Cherry
T7 John Dowie Crab Apple
T8 Fruit & Nut (Almond/Victoria Plum/Denniston Plum)
T9 Fan Oulins Golden Gage
A1 Buddleia/Rhubarb/Blackberry/Loganberry
A2 Clematis/Rosa Rugosa/Herbs
A3 Herbs
A4 Hot Dry Herb Bed
A5 Red & Whitecurrant/Climbing Rose/Tayberry/Clematis
A6 Raspberries/Gooseberries/Blackcurrant/Sallets/Herbs
A7 Pollen Shrubs
A8 Rhubarb/Mints/Honeysuckle
R1-4 Rotation Beds 1-4
C Comfrey
CT Comfrey Tub
ABR Trellis Covered Arbor Seat
HB/C Hot-Box/Compost Box
GH Lean-To Greenhouse
ST Strawberry Tower
WT Water Tank
P Small Pond
PT Potato Tyre Towers
H Horseradish
S Perennial Sallets

Neighbour's Garage

Parking Spaces

Front Lawn

Parking Space

N

Bathroom

Hall

Day-Room

Bedroom

Kitchen

0   1   5   10m

28

High Wycombe

Address
Three Doves
41 Partridge Way
Downley
HIGH WYCOMBE
Buckinghamshire
HP13 5JX

Telephone
(0494) 534198

Contact
Daphne Watson

Date est.
1990

Size/acres
0.06

Residents
4

Visitors
BA

Most of my time has been spent on the house, which needed a new more efficient gas boiler, hot water tank and thermostatic radiator taps, damp proofing of lower back walls below soil level, resurfacing of balcony and elevated path to back garden. The attic and walls required insulation, windows were already double glazed. The whole house needed redecorating and much repair – kitchen still a disaster area.

Compost bins, a tumbler and worm bin were installed early on to take a large amount of material needing clearing – five large unproductive trees, suckering sumach and kerria, strangling bindweed and cleavers and a neighbour's overhanging trees. These have been cut back to create a relatively sunny glade with woodland edge in the north facing back garden.

Many fruit trees and shrubs along with herbs, vegetables and traditional cottage garden and wild plants have been planted through mulch. Pumpkins and sweetcorn have been most prolific. Most of the fruit trees and climbers are being trained up the recently erected fences. The ponds are partly dug. Rain water butts were put in at an early stage at the back and front of the house as well as on the balcony and have proved most useful whilst establishing plants in our dry summers. The greenhouse has been put in a sunny spot at the bottom of the garden against a wall. The balcony has provided almost all our salad, herb and strawberry needs for two summers, with ample space left for lounging in the sun. The garden should be very productive by 1994.

If I come up on the Pools I'll put in solar panels, a glass porch on the sunny side and a wood burning stove before finding a rural retreat and starting all over again!

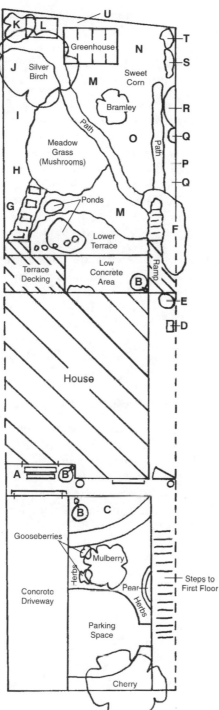

A Balcony – salads, herbs, strawberries, beans & flowers
B Water butts
C Grape, thrift, hollyhocks, blackcurrant, wisteria
D Worm bin
E Herb pot
F Rose, honeysuckle, clematis, lavender
G Morello cherry
H Spring bulbs
I Blackcurrants, ramsons
J Comfrey patch + borage, tree onions, climbing beans, nasturtiums
K Holly
L Compost bins
M Strawberries, herbs
N Raspberries, tayberry
O Herbs, gooseberries, pumpkins
P Triple cherry unusual fruit and nuts
Q Climbing beans
R Triple apple
S Mallow
T Lilac
U Triple peach

29

Higham Marsh

Address
*Marsh Cottage
Higham Marsh
Stoke-by-Nayland
COLCHESTER
CO6 4SX*

Telephone
(0206) 37326

Contact
*John van der Post,
Maryjane Preece*

Date est.
1991

Size/acres
0.7

Residents
2

Visitors
BA

Amidst the mad monoculturalism of East Anglia, our plot seems like a spot of sanity even in its embryonic stages. Marsh Cottage used to be on a marsh until the land was drained so well that now water has to be pumped continuously onto the crops.

We caretake a subsiding, damp, energy-inefficient house (two south facing windows, four north facing) and a lovely, wild rampaging garden. The garden had been left fallow for about twenty years before we moved here and the northern half had been planted with a good variety of native deciduous trees, now about ten years old. We started developing our plot last year (1991) by getting four chickens to help us work the land; we now have a workforce and food supply of thirty!

The house is south facing with most of the garden behind it. Out front was a compacted gravelly driveway. We have built a raised mulch bed on it with an old carpet as a barrier, big beams as the edges and a variety of manures to make soil. At the back, the garden is surrounded on three sides by a wide ditch where we have a polytunnel and the beginnings of a forest garden. On the higher land near the house we have an enclosed annual garden and fruit bush area, a herb area and a part-time roof water stream growing watercress.

Our main climatic feature is the wind – due to approximately a mile without any shelter to the west. Unfortunately we can't afford a wind generator to take advantage of this, but we are preparing for when the surrounding fields blow towards us by planting thick hedges. Our long term aims for this place are to build a strong healthy garden that will be one of the pockets of life to work out from when the land around us has turned to desert.

Kerhilley is a house with a large garden – just over 0.5 acre – on the outskirts of a small town in the Surrey commuter belt. We have grown fruit and vegetables here for 34 years by a minimum dig method and without using any artificial chemicals or animal fertilisers since our last chicken died over 20 years ago.

Five years ago we decided to work towards self-sufficiency in food in the hope of showing that two elderly vegans could produce all the food they really needed from a small acreage with their own manual labour and hardly any bought in materials. It is said that a vegan can live on the food from a fifth of an acre. We consider extra ground is needed to grow compost material to maintain soil fertility. Our garden is about the right size for our project.

We feel it is wrong to use food from countries where people are hungry: many because they have lost their land to exporters. Moreover locally produced food can be more health promoting. Resources used in preservatives, packaging and transport are saved.

In a world of exploding population and dwindling resources, especially of water and fertile land, the phasing out of livestock farming is essential. It yields nothing, not even fertiliser, that cannot be got more economically direct from plants. And it is wrong to enslave fellow creatures.

We grow our vegetables in four feet wide strips with one foot paths between. The strips are not trodden, so little labour is required for cultivation. The paths grow compost material.

In 1986, inspired by Robert Hart, we started to grow soft fruit and perennial herbs beneath the old fruit and nut trees in the northwest corner of the garden. The 1987 storm felled most of the trees! We've planted new ones and hope to develop a forest garden as they mature.

Three out of four mature hazels survived the storm and we have planted more, some to be trained espalier fashion so that we can net them from squirrels. Hazel nuts, various beans and peas, sunflower, maize and quinoa seeds and potatoes yield ample protein. We grow a great variety of fruits and vegetables, including grapes,

30

Kerhilley

Address
Movement for Compassionate Living
47 Highlands Road
LEATHERHEAD
Surrey
KT22 8NQ

Telephone
(0372) 372389

Contact
Kathleen & Jack Jannaway

Date est.
1958

Size/acres
0.5

Residents
2

Visitors
BA

tomatoes, peppers, cucumbers and winter lettuce in our two greenhouses. All give some protein as well as vitamins, minerals, trace elements and energy.

We keep the soil fertile with compost and the winter tares that we sow on the ground cleared in the Autumn. We use comfrey liquid fertiliser.

We are bringing more land into cultivation each year and now have no doubt that we could achieve self-sufficiency in food if we had the time to give to gardening that we now give to running an educational charity, the Movement for Compassionate Living, the Vegan Way.

We plan to leave areas for wild life and have this year made a pond to attract water creatures – especially frogs to eat slugs!

We realise that we have much to learn and appreciate the help and encouragement of the permaculture movement.

We offer a variety of home produced leaflets and booklets on our work and welcome visitors by arrangement but cannot offer accommodation.

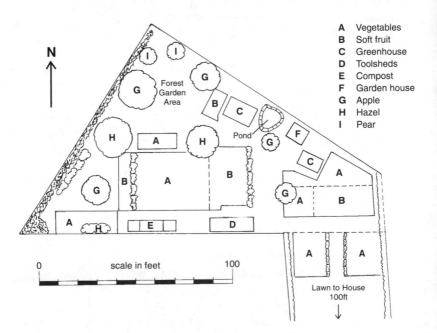

A   Vegetables
B   Soft fruit
C   Greenhouse
D   Toolsheds
E   Compost
F   Garden house
G   Apple
H   Hazel
I   Pear

Kingston Permaculture has rented a one acre plot of land on which a sustainable organic food producing system is being established. The site is part of the Knollmead allotments in Tolworth, Surrey. The work is carried out by volunteers meeting every other Sunday.

On the site we have created:

- A forest garden and woodland glade areas.
- Wildlife ponds (puddled with clay) with ditches.
- Vegetable beds with keyhole paths.
- Native fruiting hedgerows and a 'dead hedge'.
- A herb spiral.
- A geodesic frame (vertical growing frame for beans).
- A greenhouse with attached timber earth-bermed shelter.
- Compost bins.

The Knollmead Project will be very much an educational centre and an example of how our environment can be greatly improved by careful, considered design. The project is grant aided, in part by Kingston Borough Council, Shell Better Britain and English Nature.

Knollmead

Address
c/o 163 Hook Rise South SURBITON Surrey KT6 7NA

Telephone
081-397 7827

Contact
Pooran Desai

Date est.
1990

Size/acres
1

Residents
None .

Visitors
BA, working Sundays

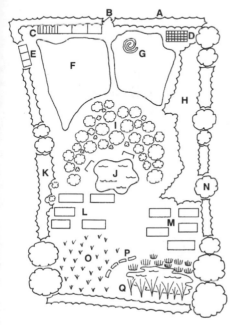

A	Fruit hedge
B	Entrance
C	Lean-to & pergola
D	Shed
E	Compost bins
F	Vegetable bed
G	Herb spiral & lawn area
H	Hazel & willow coppice
I	Forest garden
J	Pond
K	Fruit hedge
L	Demonstration plots (sunny)
M	Demonstration plots (shady)
N	Existing hedgerow
O	Wild flower meadow
P	Beehives
Q	Reed bed

32

Redfield

Address
*Redfield
Community
Buckingham Road
Winslow
BUCKINGHAM
MK18 3LZ*

Telephone
(0296) 712161

Contact
Simon Pratt

Date est.
1978

Size/acres
17

Residents
34

Visitors
BA,WWOOF

Redfield Community is home to around 20 adults and their children. Every adult is a member and tenant of the *Redley Housing Co-operative* which owns the property. Every member has equal power and responsibility in the management of the co-op, decisions are made by consensus at the weekly meeting. The community has 17 acres of land around a large Victorian house and stable block, including a 7 acre field, 4 acres of woodland, orchard, ponds, organic vegetable and herb gardens. We grow a proportion of our fruit and vegetables and are self-sufficient in firewood.

Permaculture principles and techniques are being introduced here as part of the overall development of the site. In the last two years the following have been established:

- A small orchard with free ranging chickens.
- Permaculture demonstration garden surrounded by fruiting hedges.
- Herb spiral.
- Nineteen walnut trees planted.
- A new hedge across the field, nearly 500 plants.
- Clearance and replanting of degraded woodland.
- Forest garden planted.

In the future, we hope to focus on our water and energy systems:

- Collecting rainwater from our roofs.
- Converting our existing gravel filter bed into a reed bed system for sewage treatment.
- Installing a new efficient heating system, possibly including solar panels and Kachel-ovens.

All these new developments plus maintenance of existing systems need a continuous input of time and money. If you would like to join us or contribute in any way, please make contact. We now have an extensive programme of courses, including permaculture, in the recently completed *Redfield Centre* – please write for details.

*Plum tree used as runner bean support surrounded by comfrey and
blackcurrant plants as a mutually beneficial guild, Redfield*

33

Reigate

Address
The Bungalow
Shagbrook
Main Road
REIGATE
Surrey
RH2 9RE

Telephone
(0737) 248909

Contact
Meike

Date est.
1984

Size/acres
3.5

Residents
4

Visitors
BA,WWOOF

Originally, the smallholding belonged to the head gardener of Shagbrook, a Victorian residence. He bought 'his' kitchen garden and the blue, tree-lined once exotic walk around the stone-walled pond which led to an orchard. That area is now used as paddocks for sheep and geese as well as the main vegetable garden. He converted the brick store-house into his residence and two extensions since then have made it big enough to house a small community.

Change has been a constant. No more striving for self-sufficiency or harvesting for the weekly W.I. and market stalls. The expensive Soil Association symbol has been relinquished, the hedge re-laid and inter-planted, polytunnel abandoned, free-range ducks ravaged by the foxes and the last of the kale demolished by persistently invasive rabbits. (Two local guns and the resident cat occasionally lie in wait to deal with this problem.) The hens still scratch the Winter soil in the herb patch.

Since a Permaculture Design Course, held here in August 1991, there are undulating edges, butts full of rainwater, a pond in a frost pocket and salads/herbs nestle successfully under plum, mulberry, quince, cherry and pear trees. Honey is shared with the beekeeper from down the road who also gives demonstrations to visitors. The vegetable garden is encouraged to supply more of its own seedlings for well-established perennial beds.

People care is more important than garden care now. The interest to supply others with food is dwindling unless they take an active part in the process. This would be a place for a mini Community Supported Agriculture. The sharing of knowledge, skills, life-skills, time, space and food is nurtured. Long and short-term WWOOFers feel inspired by this new way of life, attitudes and approaches according to the visitors book. They still use our compost loos. No smell. No mess. Anyone interested is offered guided tours in return for shared work.

My dissertation on *Feasible Fibres* was incorporated into *Feasible Fibres into Surrey*, a flax initiative. Anyone with interest or expertise, please contact Meike.

Rosehill is a house in The Green Belt set in about 7 acres or so. The garden around the house consists of 3-4 acres of lawns and a heart shaped rose garden – also a lake which I am putting fish in from time to time. I have planted twenty fruit trees in the top lawn but have not yet developed stacking into a forest garden.

I am kept mainly to a half acre paddock which is pretty wild and productive. We don't need compost but I do take horse manure from our neighbours to get it off their hands and prevent them from burning it. The bottom field is about 1.5 acres, a wilderness into which I may introduce species, though the blackberries there are one of the best foods in the whole world. There is an acre or two of woodland which has one or two old oaks, a horse chestnut and plenty of ash and sycamore (I cut the odd one for growing mushrooms on logs). Started Bonfils grain plot in summer 1992 which I believe provides the key to getting permaculture established on large areas through good annual yields without much work whilst the permanent crops are established.

Other things I'm trying include:

- Jean Pain compost/heater for greenhouse.
- Dug out/cave/house prototype.

Other possibilities are compost loo, natural swimming pool, reed bed. This winter I will take cuttings of willow, plant close together in two rows to make a natural wall which I have heard can be used for houses without planning permission.

Future plans:

- Propagating perennials, shrubs, trees and unusual stuff.

- Do a massive grain plot on 100 to 2000 acres and show that the land can be used sustainably financially as well – use the profits to establish perennial agriculture.

Visitors are really welcome to come and share ideas and enthusiasm.

34

Rosehill

Address
*Rosehill
Great Amwell
WARE
Hertfordshire
SG12 9SQ*

Telephone
*(0920) 871037
or 871661*

Contact
Peter Ratcliff

Date est.
1990

Size/acres
7

Residents
3

Visitors
BA

35

Shrubb Farm Cottages

Address
*Shrubb Farm
Cottages
Larling
East Harling
NORWICH
NR16 2QT*

Telephone
(0953) 717844

Contact
*Tim Bastable,
Molly O'Brien*

Date est.
1991

Size/acres
1

Residents
9

Visitors
BA

Home to a community since 1968, Shrubb is an anachronism in post-Thatcherite Britain. The 17th century cottage is a working example of stewardship. Owned by Shrubb Family Ltd., all community members are directors of the company – new members pay no capital on joining and take no money on leaving. In spite of this hopelessly idealistic management system, the buildings and community have prospered and even survived a major fire in the early 1980s.

By pure chance three newcomers to the community are permaculture design course graduates and the process of 'perming' Shrubb began in spring 1992. Our 1 acre plot certainly presents a challenge. It's surrounded by typical East Anglian wheatlands, with few trees and very little hedgerow. The badly degraded breckland soil, sandy and shallow, overlies boulder clay which in turn covers chalk bedrock. It turns to dust in summer and compacts with amazing ease in winter. As a bonus all the cultivated areas were badly infested with perennial weeds.

Our main priorities last year were the production of perennial plants, controlling weeds and improving soil condition and fertility. 20 tons of farm manure were composted and incorporated into the soil, some intensive areas were double dug to break up the clay pan, mechanically remove weed roots and prepare 'no-dig' beds. Much of our food production last year was from annual vegetables and whilst we don't see this changing much in the immediate future we have produced a good range of herbs, some fruit bushes, plant protectors and some edible perennials.

Major tasks to do are planting out several hundred trees in zone five, completing our intensive area as a full-on circle bed, establishing a polytunnel, setting up a grey water management system and forest garden, building a pond and some trials of mulching techniques on pernicious British weeds.

We welcome visitors who enjoy working and want to gain practical experience and help develop temperate permacultural techniques. We have many skills to share – not least good food, laughter and music. If you would like to visit Shrubb Family please contact us well in advance.

Springhill Farm is 186 acres in the attractive valley of the River Thame and has been organic since 1946. Approximately one-third of the farm has been planted to mixed wood/fruit/bush and coppice designed with help from Andy Langford. Stock now beef and sheep may include rare breeds, weeder geese and deer. A vegetable growing club has just been started and is exploring the principles and practicality of subscription farming. There is scope for anyone seriously interested in permaculture to become actively involved. Various types of accommodation may be available on long lease or time-share basis, some with individual or group responsibility for particular areas.

Springhill Centre is a therapeutic community including some recovering from chronic illnesses. An agroforestry project supervised by Silsoe College makes it possible for one or two grant aided students to work a place-ment year at Springhill. We are moving towards increasing participation with serious students of planetary custodianship.

Objectives of the Springhill Vegetable Club:

* Supply of organically grown vegetables for members, and for those in particular need, i.e. those with allergies to chemicals.

* Demonstration of subscription farming principles and responsible stewardship through the principles of permaculture, organic gardening and bio-dynamics.

* Research into techniques and development of these principles.

* Gradual planned expansion into full scale subscription farming, to include bush fruit, top fruit, wool, milk, poultry.

* Education through open days, liaison with schools and young people, student projects, rare breeds.

* Processing of selected vegetables e.g. sauerkraut, salted cucumbers, wine.

* Improvement of fertility and amenity of land used.

* Encouragement of others to emulate subscription gardening principles.

36

Springhill

Address
Springhill Centre
Cuddington Road
Dinton
AYLESBURY
Buckinghamshire
HP18 0AD

Telephone
(0296) 748278

Contact
Hugh Coates

Date est.
1990

Size/acres
186

Residents
8

Visitors
BA, WWOOF

37

West Wood

Address
c/o 15 Rotten Row
Riseley
BEDFORD
MK44 1EJ

Telephone

Contact
Mark Powell

Date est.
1990

Size/acres
200

Residents
None

Visitors
BA

West Wood is a 200 acre ancient wood owned by the Forestry Commission. The canopy was clear felled in the 1930s and replanted with oaks. The understorey and ground flora retain the diversity of an ancient semi-natural woodland. I buy the standing undergrowth and also the oak thinnings and undertake to coppice them and extract the usable material. My main and most profitable product is thatching spars, of which I can generally get about 50,000 from a hectare. These retail at about £60 per thousand. This yield is well below that from prime hazel coppices because the undergrowth is partially derelict and has been locally shaded out during the denser earlier decades of plantation oaks. Improving the productivity of the coppice will be a gradual process of thinning the canopy and increasing the density of coppice stools using natural regeneration and layering. I have accumulated a fair amount of information and experience of these methods and will happily correspond about these and other factors which are important to the success of commercial coppicing including deterring deer browsing, disposal/uses of waste brash, quick and easy bramble control and sensitive ways of keeping rides passable. I produce a whole range of other coppice products including charcoal, firewood, hedging stakes and binders, pea sticks and rustic poles.

Over the past couple of years I have been experimenting with multistorey cropping, wild foods and no-dig gardening. I have tried acorns (left on the lid of my charcoal kiln overnight), honey fungus, edible ornamentals (day lily, honesty, shepherds purse, hairy bittercress) and leaf curd. I mix the curd with oatmeal, onion and herbs to make 'leaf-burgers'. They are more than just edible; they are actually very pleasant, but require a fair amount of work for the amount of food produced. A much more significant proportion of my food comes from 'carrion' (e.g. road casualties) and from 'gleanings' – I have agreements with a local farmer to buy up cheaply the crops he cannot sell because of gluts or slight blemishes and I sometimes barter half a days labour for permission to take whatever I want of a crop that is about to be ploughed in. While not strictly permacultural I see this as a stepping stone stage, accustoming my body to a more vegetable based diet and weaning myself off bread, biscuits and choccy bars.

The site, near Coombe Martin, is a 1.5 acre steep valley pasture surrounded by mixed deciduous and conifer woodland. The design centres around a possible future site of habitation (unlikely in reality because of the planning laws), marked 'Hut site' on the drawing (*see next page*). The location of this site was carefully calculated such that the site obtains the maximum possible amount of winter sun.

The design aims are:

1. To establish tree cover on most of the site.
2. To use a wide diversity of useful species.
3. For the system to need minimal maintenance.

Initial planting took place in 1989, with over 2200 trees and shrubs of over 200 species planted. Further underplanting of shrubs, ground cover species etc. will take place as appropriate. The areas of medium and large sized trees are interplanted with nurse trees such as *Thuja plicata* (Western red cedar) and *Prunus avium* (cherry) which will be removed and the timber used in 10-15 years.

Species used include:

- Outer native areas – alders, willows, aspen by stream; birch, ash, rowan, hawthorn etc.
  Also edible bamboos by stream.
- Evergreen trees – pines (edible pine nuts), evergreen oaks.
- Large crop trees – walnuts, chestnuts, hickories, beech, wingnut, pears.
- Medium crop trees – apples, pears, plums on vigorous rootstocks; pines, mulberries.
- Small crop trees – filberts, cobnuts, fig, persimmons, *amelanchier*, *cornus* spp., apples, pears and plums on dwarf rootstocks.

Weed control has been achieved by using black plastic mulch squares, approximately 800 x 800mm, placed around trees over existing pasture. Tree establishment has been excellent, despite the first two summers being hot and dry. Maintenance has been minimal; no weeding or pruning has been carried out. Most trees are growing well and some have started to crop already.

S & SW ENGLAND

38

Agroforestry Research Trust

Address
Agroforestry Research Trust
17 Arden Drive
Chelston
TORQUAY
Devon
TQ2 6DZ

Telephone

Contact
Martin Crawford

Date est.
1989

Size/acres
1.5

Residents
None

Visitors
BA,
no accommodation

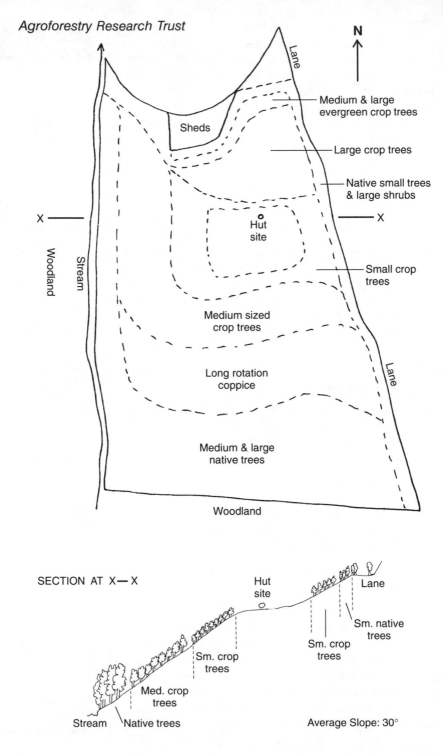

Agroforestry Research Trust

N

Medium & large
evergreen crop trees

Large crop trees

Native small trees
& large shrubs

Small crop
trees

Hut
site

Medium sized
crop trees

Long rotation
coppice

Medium & large
native trees

Sheds

Woodland

Stream

Lane

Lane

X — X

Woodland

SECTION AT X—X

Hut
site

Lane

Sm. native
trees

Sm. crop
trees

Sm. crop
trees

Med. crop
trees

Native trees

Stream

Average Slope: 30°

I selected a long, thin allotment running along a South facing wall, that looked like it hadn't been cultivated for many seasons and hence would be very fertile. My objective was to be self-sufficient in vegetables, starting as soon as possible. The problem was that it was already 28 March and the plot, just rented and rotovated, was full of chopped couch, nettles, bindweed, docks and dandelion. I decided to see how quickly hoeing and weeding could tame the land. I had no mulch materials to hand and anyway they take land out of action for a season, except for the coarser crops. The ground was unweedable, being much too claggy at the time. But I put in potatoes anyway and also ten shrivelled Jerusalem artichokes from the greengrocer. As the ground gradually warmed up and dried out, from early April, I chop-hoed the weeds as they emerged.

I then planted shallots, early in April, two months beyond their ideal planting time. Here I made a very interesting mistake. As time was short, I decided to pop them straight into rotovated but unweeded ground, covered with a little loose soil. Within five weeks some of them provided me with my first harvest, of green 'spring onions'. They grew blithely unaware, as I was, that I had already dibbled potatoes into the same ground! No problem on root space, I thought, as they would be utilising different soil layers; but the potatoes would soon shade the shallots. In fact, little was lost; two crops were harvested in quick succession from unweeded land – possibly the highest production for the least effort I have yet achieved.

I was able to chop-hoe other potato patches six times between planting and crop emergence early in May. This effort was absolutely crucial, to knock back all emerging couch and dandelions. Hot weather then quickly helped the haulms to cover and shade out any weeds. The land certainly wasn't perfectly clean by harvest, but the potatoes had won and remaining weed was easily forked out. The unpromising Jerusalem artichokes had the same treatment and have yielded very heavily.

My methods were a gamble with the weather, but they came up trumps. I spent 5-6 hours a week at the allotment over the first two months, completing the main cultivations by 24 May.

S & SW ENGLAND

39

Bath

Address
c/o 11 Junction Avenue
BATH
BA2 3NJ

Telephone
(0225) 466168

Contact
Helen Woodley

Date est.
1992

Size/acres
0.03

Residents
None

Visitors
BA

40

Crippets

Address
*Crippets
Bucks Mills
BIDEFORD
Devon
EX39 5DZ*

Telephone
(0237) 431632

Contact
*David Gale,
Jennifer Greenway*

Date est.
1990

Size/acres
0.08

Residents
2

Visitors
BA

The permaculture plot at Crippets consists of a small 17th century stone and cob (mud) fishing cottage with 1/8 acre of land in the small hamlet of Buck's Mills on the North Devon coast. The plot faces southeast and is situated on a plateau overlooking the hamlet at a point where the valley meets the sea and is surrounded by native woodland.

The plot has been designed along permaculture principles and is in its third year of implementation. The various strategies in the garden include: mini forest garden (which has been adopted by the woodland and its wildlife), perennial and self-seeding annual vegetables, salad and fruit, several stone raised beds, herbs and hedge species, fungi, pond, and a chicken tractor system is planned for the future.

As well as obtaining a high proportion of produce from our land, we also harvest food and organic fertilisers from the sea. We are currently carrying out research into mariculture (shoreline permaculture) and hope to hold an introductory course in the future.

The building is in the process of being renovated and has also been designed along permaculture principles. The strategies used include: increasing energy efficiency, use of renewable energies, use of materials from sustainable sources, use of organic materials that do not pollute in their manufacture or use and can be recycled, use of local materials and skills, rain and spring water collection.

The landscape and building work have been designed by the permaculture design practice Gale & Snowden,

who provide a full permaculture design service in architecture, landscapes and interiors. Their services range from concept reports and feasibility studies to help with planning applications and building regulations, through to working drawings and construction coordination. They can be contacted at 32 Queen Street, Barnstaple, Devon EX32 8HQ. Tel: (0271) 326638.

H yden House is a family house and the home of *Permaculture Magazine*. The dwelling consists of two converted 19th century flint cottages set in half an acre of land on the edge of the South Downs. When we moved here in 1986, the back garden was the size of a pocket handkerchief. In 1991, we managed to acquire 0.3 acre of intensively farmed arable land adjoining the back garden. The plot is 65 by 20 metres, sloping gently east towards the house.

Our first move was to sow a wildflower mix (Cricklade SSSI mix) over the entire site to cover the eroded soil. This has now given three years of spectacular show. Following this, we planted 700 mixed indigenous hedgerow trees, many of which are food bearing, to create an eventual windbreak and border the site.

With the assistance of Chris Hoppe of Earthcare Designs, we put together an overall design strategy for the site. Already established are the composting systems, mulched vegetable garden and the annual, spring and summer meadows. The spring meadow is placed nearest the house and cut to provide a children's play area through the summer months. Sixty fruit and nut bearing trees have also been planted on different root stocks to eventually create a multi-layered canopy. The area of trees on the north side of the plot will form the upper levels of a forest garden, whilst those on the west and south sides will be managed as an orchard with underlying summer meadow. On the west border, a number of fast growing trees have been planted to provide timber for heating and enhance the windbreak. Several wood piles have also been introduced to provide increased habitat diversity and the area in the northwest corner has been left for wilderness.

We have built a ramp from the lower garden into the spring meadow, creating terraced beds for a salad garden, and we now have a bee colony and the start of our chicken system. We will be building a number of small ponds and will eventually build a large pond sited in the summer meadow.

We have also helped start a Local Exchange Trading System and, together with a number of friends, are creating many permacultural links in the local community.

41

Hyden House

Address
Hyden House
Little Hyden Lane
Clanfield
PORTSMOUTH
Hampshire
PO8 0RU

Telephone
(0705) 596500

Contact
Tim & Maddy Harland

Date est.
1991

Size/acres
0.5

Residents
4

Visitors
BA,
no accommodation

Hyden House

Prevailing SW Wind

A   House
B   Patio
C   Wood store
D   Greenhouse
E   Herb/salad bed
F   Terraced salad beds
G   Chicken run
H   Spring wildflower meadow
    & children's play area
I   Vegetable garden
J   Compost heaps
K   Earth mound
L   Annual wildflower meadow
M   Summer wildflower meadow
N   Forest garden
O   Mixed hedgerow
    Fruit or nut trees

0   20   40
scale in feet

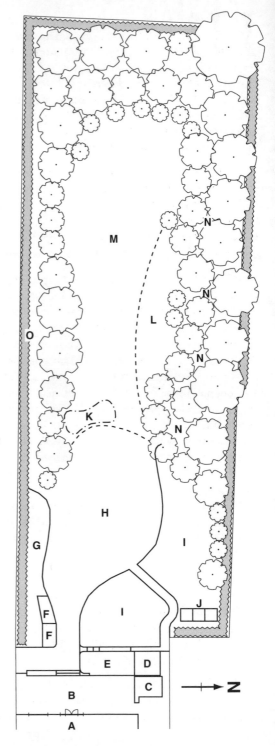

Keveral Farm has been a community since 1972. Its present incarnation revolves round a housing co-op called One Community and a workers co-op called Keveral Farmers.

One Community rents a large farmhouse from a London based housing association. The nine adults and three children live in the house or caravans next to it. The house is managed by the residents, many of whom hope to steer its management towards a more sustainable lifestyle. There is a weekly house meeting at which decisions are made by a two-thirds majority if a consensus cannot be reached.

Keveral Farmers are based on the 30 acres of leased land adjoining the house. There is a livery stables, a blacksmiths forge, a semi converted barn for visitors and assorted outbuildings at the farm. We keep chickens and ducks for their free range eggs and 3 goats and 2 sheep for their company. There is pasture land for the horses, woodland for firewood and 3 polytunnels and a half acre vegetable plot for food. The whole farm has the Soil Association organic standard and we are replanting an orchard with traditional varieties.

A disused walled garden is being brought back to life by a permaculture design, along with spreading permaculture principles through an introductory course and the setting up of a local group. We are facilitating environmental education by encouraging kids' camps to come here and providing resources for them to use.

Camping is available and we take volunteers.

42

Keveral Farm

Address
Keveral Farm
Seaton
LOOE
Cornwall
PL13 1PA

Telephone
(05035) 215

Contact
Oak, Steve,
Tracy

Date est.
1972

Size/acres
30

Residents
8

Visitors
BA

43

Little Ash

Address
Little Ash Eco Farm
Throwleigh
OKEHAMPTON
Devon
EX20 2HY

Telephone
(064723) 394

Contact
Marthe Kiley-Worthington

Date est.
1983

Size/acres
80

Residents
3

Visitors
BA, WWOOF

Little Ash Ecological Farm is 60 acres of grade 2/3 land and 20 hired acres. It has a 4 acre mixed deciduous woodland, 2 acres of field vegetables and fruit. It has two permanently running streams and a couple of ponds. 10 acres of arable cereal crops are grown annually (approximately 2 acres wheat, 3 oats, 5 barley and dredge corn, small area of trial maize 1989, linseed 1990, naked oats and triticale 1991) and rotated with the 60 acres or so of grass which is carefully managed. It is divided by double fences and establishing hedges into some 12 paddocks. The farm thus has a range of natural and managed habitats. It is run in conjunction with Little Druimghigha, a 70 acre eco-croft on the Isle of Mull, Argyll.

The objectives for the development of Little Ash are to develop it as a productive efficient farm with a sound financial basis, but also a farming practice that is sympathetic to the environment of the National Park and which in addition efficiently produces food and a living for the farmers without inputs to the system, increases rurally based employment and provide limited educational and recreational facilities without any environmental detriment. The whole farm is a conservation area. It is 'ultramodern' agriculture for the 21st century.

An ecological farm is defined as 'self-sustaining, diversified, high yielding, socially, ethically and aesthetically acceptable and causing no long term or irreversible environmental changes'. Airy fairy? No, we have demonstrated that this is possible on two previous farms, one in Sussex and one in the Hebrides over the last 18 years. At Little Ash we are not only developing and running an ecological farm, but also experimenting with ecological living for the farmers by reducing resources for housing, producing our own power etc.

In 1974 Lower Shaw Farm was standing empty and unused and the outbuildings were barely fit for cows let alone humans. Since then the dairy and sheds have been converted to dormitories, meeting rooms and workshops and the garden worked organically. Thanks to the enthusiasm and effort of residents and visitors a sense of communal continuity has been established. There are now six adults and seven children living in the farmhouse; while the 'farm' itself is run as a meeting place for weekend and week-long courses, conferences and learning holidays. It has a steady stream of visitors throughout the year.

Lower Shaw Farm is now a three acre 'oasis' in an area of 1990's 'development'. Despite the loss of green fields, the farm has retained its character and atmosphere; and not far away is open countryside.

In January 1992 we hosted a workshop for permaculture design students wishing to gain practical experience. The result of this course was a comprehensive design which we are now implementing stage by stage. So far, we have made a people-friendly, mound-surrounded, circle of grass for bonfires, dancing etc.; have planted fruit trees as the beginnings of a forest garden; have plans for a fruit and nut bearing hedge; and have a circular vegetable plot with mulched keyhole beds. We plan to construct a polytunnel warmed and irrigated by grey water from the house and an 'eco' bathroom with compost toilets and solar heated showers. Our poultry will be moving to a new henhouse constructed next to a greenhouse.

About once a month we have voluntary working weekends run in conjunction with WWOOF and these are suitable times for people interested in the project to visit. We have a programme of activities which we will happily send on receipt of an s.a.e..

S & SW ENGLAND

44

Lower Shaw Farm

Address
Lower Shaw Farm
Old Shaw Lane
Shaw
SWINDON
SN5 9PJ

Telephone
(0793) 771080

Contact
Andrea Hirsch

Date est.
1974

Size/acres
3.2

Residents
13

Visitors
BA, WWOOF

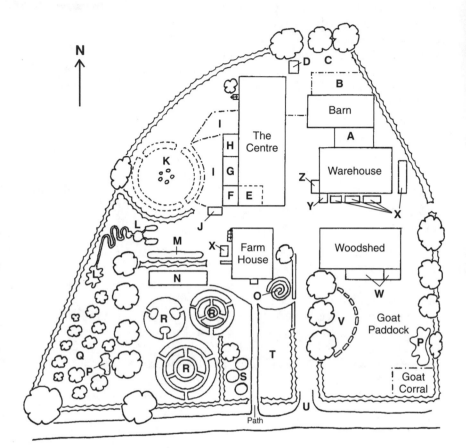

A	Covered yard	**N**	Polytunnel
B	Volleyball court	**O**	Herb spiral
C	Children's recreation area	**P**	Pond
D	Shed	**Q**	Forest garden
E	Eco-bathroom with compost toilet & solar heated water system	**R**	Vegetable plots
F	Milking shed	**S**	Children's vegetable plots with central ponds
G	Goat stalls	**T**	Wildflower meadow
H	Pony stable	**U**	Main entrance
I	Concrete livestock enclosure	**V**	Parking area
J	Shed	**W**	Chicken/greenhouse
K	The Henge – stones & fireplace	**X**	Caravans
L	Reed beds	**Y**	Coalshed
M	Compost heap	**Z**	Toolshed

T he Monkey Sanctuary was established in 1964 to provide a stimulating environment for woolly monkeys rescued from lives of isolation in zoos or as pets and was the first place they bred in captivity. Eventually it is hoped to return the colony to their native Amazonian rainforest habitat, however wild woolly monkeys are threatened by hunting and habitat destruction. The Monkey Sanctuary educates its many visitors and school groups about the need for conservation of the rainforest and native wildlife, for which most of its grounds are managed. Most of the workers, including volunteers, live on site as a community.

In 1992 it was decided to make the Monkey Sanctuary more self reliant in terms of food, energy, water etc.. Also the educational aims were widened to cover the promotion of ecologically sensitive/sustainable living. A permaculture design is being drawn up and work implementation has begun. Forest garden areas will provide fruit, greens, etc. for monkeys and people and demonstrate permaculture principles to the public. It is hoped to use waste wood shavings, food and faeces from the monkey territory and human excreta to generate methane. The energy efficiency of the buildings will be improved and thermal energy from composting wood chips (from woodland management) may be used. Plant based grey and black water treatment, rainwater collection and re-use of water is also being considered. The Monkey Sanctuary seeks to buy locally grown organic food and support other local businesses.

The Monkey Sanctuary is open to the public April to October when one forest garden can be seen, but those specifically wanting to see all the forest garden areas should do so by prior arrangement (summer or winter). Residential volunteers help care for the monkeys and in Summer work with visitors. Gardening, maintenance and construction work is done during the winter. Can you help? People with relevant skills particularly welcome.

45

Monkey Sanctuary

Address
Monkey Sanctuary
LOOE
Cornwall
PL13 1NZ

Telephone
(0793) 771080

Contact
Carole Gale

Date est.
1992

Size/acres
12

Residents
8

Visitors
BA, working volunteers

46

Plants For A Future

Address
The Field
Higher Penpoll
St Veep
LOSTWITHIEL
Cornwall
PL22 0NG

Telephone
(0208) 873554
or 873263

Contact
Addy, Jenny

Date est.
1990

Size/acres
20

Residents
4

Visitors
BA

Plants For A Future is a vegan alternative plant project that has recently started in Cornwall. Its aim is to demonstrate the wide variety of useful commodities such as food, fibres, medicines etc. that can be obtained from plants grown outdoors in temperate regions. We have 28 acres of south facing but exposed land. We have planted 12 acres of woodland and a mile or so of hedges as well as over 2 acres of beds containing a rapidly increasing variety of useful and unusual plants – at present about 1750 species.

We are trying to build up a vegan community based around the plant project but at present we are unable to live on the land, having a house and a flat about 2 miles away. This community is aiming to become self-sufficient in food, fuel etc. as well as showing others that these can be derived from the plant world without recourse to animal exploitation or environmentally damaging methods. We feel that human survival depends on this and on the use of a wide variety of plant species, especially when there is a threat of rapid climatic change. Perennial plants are emphasised, because once these become established they require minimal disturbance to the soil, minimal environmental impact and minimal work.

We welcome visitors for day visits or longer stays, please ring or write before you come. We would prefer day visitors on Sundays and longer stay visitors during the first two weeks of the month, but if this is a problem let us know. We are looking for new community members, however, at present we have no permanent living space to offer.

We have a wide range of leaflets available on various aspects of plants and their uses. In Autumn 1992 we produced our first catalogue of unusual and useful seeds and plants which are available on a donations basis. We also have a leaflet detailing various projects we are working on that people might wish to invest in.

W e moved here last winter after doing a permaculture weekend at Redfield and being further inspired by a visit to Robert Hart.

The land consists of a small garden, facing southeast, and a field which slopes to the southwest. The field is sheltered from the prevailing winds by a stand of pines at the bottom; next to these we have cleared an area of brambles and planted mixed woodland of oak, ash, birch, alder, willow, hazel and rowan. This will be left as a wildlife area.

We have increased an orchard area with species suggested in *Forest Gardening* by Robert Hart to extend the apple season and are interplanting with soft fruit and herbs to make a forest garden.

The upper part of the field was laid out in small plots and we are continuing to use these for vegetables with companion planting. Overgrown plots were barriered with cardboard, compost, seaweed, horse manure and mulched with organic straw from old thatched roofs (freely available from a local thatcher).

We have planted some interesting fruits from Ken and Addy at Plants for a Future (*see opposite*) and hope to find more perennial vegetables. We are planting a small vineyard (12 vines) and this winter we are trying a potato mound (*see 'Forest Gardening' page 33*). We've been on a bee-keeping course and intend to get bees next April.

Unfortunately there is no water on the site but we have dug a pond which has already attracted several toads and lots of dragonflies.

Our aim is to create a balance between feeding ourselves (we will try anything edible) and planting native species for wildlife.

Redruth

Address
The Cottage
Tarewaste
REDRUTH
Cornwall
TR15 3SJ

Telephone
(0209) 212738

Contact
Jo Pacsoo,
Frank Cooper

Date est.
1992

Size/acres
1

Residents
2

Visitors
BA

48

South Molton

Address
*21 Churchill
Crescent
SOUTH MOLTON
Devon
EX36 4EL*

Telephone
(0769) 573272

Contact
Susan Grime

Date est.
1991

Size/acres
0.016

Residents
2

Visitors
BA

The site consists of zones 0 and 1, on heavy clay soil. The back garden faces south-south-west – it was dug over to break up the clay pan and I have laid paths on the most walked areas. There is a small annual garden, a patio and a perennial garden. The latter consists of soft fruit bushes, herbs, perennial vegetables and edible wild plants. Forest garden ideas have been used here, on a miniature scale as the garden is not large enough for trees other than the two existing ones; a beautiful young beech which grew by accident and a conifer which is my child's play tree.

The garden boasts two herb spirals, one in the small annual garden for sun lovers and one in the perennial garden for shade tolerants. Rainwater is collected from the house roof into a water butt which overflows into a bog garden, yet to be planted. Other plans include a wormery, edible fungi growing on logs and hedge clippings, a living ground cover to replace the straw mulch used at present and exotic plants in pots on the patio.

The patio has a young Brant vine climbing the north side of a home-made trellis which is also part of the washing line system. Slugs are a great problem. At present I use mechanical means of control by protecting plants with plastic shields until they are tall and well established. It works but only just.

Zone 0 is heated by locally bought wood, it contains a small plant nursery in the sitting room which has two windows facing south-south-west. A corridor which becomes a wind tunnel on windy days is used for drying herbs.

The front garden has tall shrubs around the front door which forms a porch for insulation. I have planted ivy cuttings around the walls and am waiting for them to climb, again for insulation. The remainder is grass which is cropped for the compost bin, a home-made Californian cylinder, into which also goes household vegetable waste and urine. I plan to grow soapwort in the front garden to make washing solutions.

I n a clearing beside a spring in a once wooded valley on part of the moor in southern England a house and barns were constructed using quarried stone, mud from the stream, oak from the forest and reed from the marshes. Many changes have taken place during it's and its' inhabitants evolution, bringing it back from its lengthy uninhabited derelict condition to its present residency of interested permaculturists.

The house here when purchased from its then owners (folk that had seen several generations under the same roof) had been abandoned; left for the cows to shelter in and somewhere to keep some winter feed. It was to be a lengthy project to develop the place into a Green Planet Base Play Station; somewhere that could provide education and retreat facilities which would include organic cultivation, low impact technology, animal husbandry, crafts, rural skills – permaculture etc. Somewhere that the lifestyle was so close to the earth that it would be possible to observe and learn about first hand our human interaction and interplay with all the life forms that are around us.

We are now ready to draw up plans and begin the rebuilding of a 60 x 20 foot stone barn as a Child Development Centre for some of the 'have-not' city kids. There is the possibility of including some flexible living space into the plans for anyone interested in helping.

49

South-west England

Address
*c/o Simon Pratt
(see Redfield,
entry 32)*

Telephone
(05983) 394

Contact
Chris Aldworth

Date est.
1976

Size/acres
0.5

Residents
4

Visitors
BA

50

The Anchorage

Address
The Anchorage
Salisbury Road
Broughton
STOCKBRIDGE
Hampshire
SO20 8BX

Telephone
(0794) 301234

Contact
Julie & Steven Tidy

Date est.
1983

Size/acres
3.5

Residents
4

Visitors
BA, WWOOF

The Anchorage is a commercial organic holding producing vegetables and soft fruit to Soil Association standard, sold mainly through farm gate sales and more recently Community Supported Agriculture. We are situated on a north-facing hill top on shallow loam over chalk on the edge of Salisbury Plain. Because of this our main concerns are wind and water management.

After discovering permaculture in 1990, we began transforming our holding with a rolling programme of modifications and additions. This complements our efforts of the previous ten years, to develop methods of sustainable food production and living.

We believe that permaculture is of vital importance as a survival strategy, empowering people to regain some control over their lives and thus enabling action for change. Permaculture must be freely available to everybody. We are anxious to share experiences.

A   Fruit & nut plantings
B   Main house – long term energy efficient retrofit in progress
C   Pond
D   Water tank
E   Polytunnel
F   Shed/workshop
G   Roadside sales
H   Glasshouse
I   Demonstration urban garden
J   Chicken/greenhouse
K   Wind generator
L   Solar greenhouse
M   Energy efficient bothy
N   Experimental grey water treatment
O   Pit bender
P   Chalk banks
Q   Experimental lychet
R   Walled garden
S   Compost
T   Permanent vegetable beds with fruit
U   Temporary artichoke shelterbed
V   Orchard with nuts, soft fruit & herbs
W   Pond

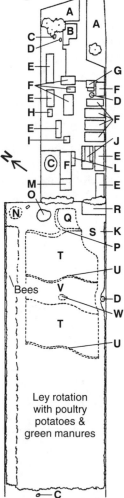

Bees

Ley rotation with poultry potatoes & green manures

A half acre site developed from bare field site in 1985 and modified as a result of Permaculture Design Course since 1990. The site slopes gently to the northwest. Soil is heavy clay. A wide range of animal and plant species have been introduced with emphasis increasingly on low maintenance and perennial crops. A small income is derived from the sale of herb plants and craft items produced on site. Features include forest garden, poultry range, polytunnels, vegetable garden and tree nursery, orchards underplanted with comfrey; deep mulch beds are lined with woven willow boundaries which then strike as cuttings. Raised bed and keyhole configurations are used as well as more intensive systems in polytunnels and zone 1. Shared ownership in woodland provides access to firewood and structural timbers. Geodesic dome and, in the coming year, a modified caravan provide workshop and occasional sleeping space.

Further orchard planting is planned for this winter (1992/3). Further workshop/meeting space are also being added. Two ponds have been constructed at low points on the site boundaries and would make excellent collecting points for run off from polytunnels and tarmac areas.

The design has been developed over the past three years and is well stocked with plant and animal species (more could be added); further design work would focus on water conservation and the use of wind and solar energies. Visitors are welcome by arrangement from spring 1993, especially those with ideas to share.

S & SW ENGLAND

51

Unicorn Cottage

Address
Unicorn Cottage
1 East Street
West Pennard
GLASTONBURY
Somerset
BA6 8NJ

Telephone
(0458) 833753

Contact
Jo & Jonathan Fryer

Date est.
1985

Size/acres
0.5

Residents
4

Visitors
BA

See overleaf for Unicorn Cottage Plan ▶

Unicorn Cottage

A Zone 1
B Forest garden
C Polytunnels
D Poultry range
E Orchards
F Deep mulch beds
G 'Fedge' – Fruiting hedge
H Ponds
I Geodesic dome
J 'Swallowed' caravan
K Coppice area

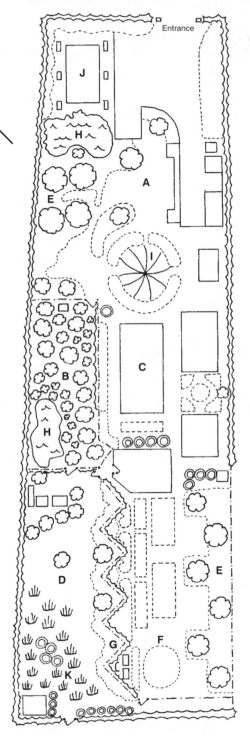

This project is an experiment in Green Architecture with the following aims:

- A wholly sustainable environment.

- To demonstrate a small cross-section of what may be possible with regard to living with Nature, living in an environment which is totally live, i.e. not built but grown, and being comfortable.

- To demonstrate that the quality of life which comes with living in such an environment is higher than is provided now.

- To provide a quiet space for rest and contemplation, which is both beautiful and practical.

- To provide a safe haven for several of wildlife, flora and fauna, which so far includes badgers, a fox, a toad, frogs, beneficial insects (e.g. hoverfly) and wild plants.

- To provide a practical start to the process of conserving the know-how, techniques and methodology of working with Nature rather than exploiting it (see video).

- To grow crops to the highest achievable standard to distribute to interested people to taste which inspires belief in people that the planet can actually pull out of the ecological dive it is in.

- To experiment with companion planting with a view to creating an environment which sustains itself.

- To provide an example of some answers to the question "What is the green alternative?", and explore several techniques with regard to achieving a 100% recycled environment.

- To prove and propagate the knowledge through work that frogs and toads are equally as important as human beings.

- To encourage, inspire and empower those whose unselfish work in trying to preserve the planet often goes unrecognised by mainstream society.

- To provide healing resources – essential oils, flower essences, herbs, quiet space used regularly by several local healing practitioners.

52

Wells

Address
c/o The Eco
Collective
33 North Road
WELLS
Somerset
BA5 2TL

Telephone

Contact
Bob Moores

Date est.
1983

Size/acres
1.8

Residents
None

Visitors
BA

- To promote ideas relating to:
    - water conservation and pollution;
    - health and hygiene without chemicals;
    - land use – rationale;
    - a productive and beautiful landscape;
    - sustainable lifestyle – research and development.

Plotting The Next Edition!

Y ou are invited to submit your entry for the 1996/7 edition of *The Permaculture Plot*.

Please follow the existing style to include:

- Address and telephone number.
- Contact name.
- Date site/project established
- Size (acres).
- Number of permanent residents.
- How people can visit:
  - welcome at all times;
  - welcome by arrangement;
  - through the WWOOF scheme (details on request);
  - cannot be accommodated;
  - no visitors, thanks.
- 300 words to describe your project.
- Plan of site – To include A4 size base plan **without** any text/key + a further A4 size copy of the same plan **with** text/key.
- Other photographs or illustrations that could be considered for including.

Please send your entry to Simon Pratt (*see address below*).

Simon Pratt
Compiler
January 1994

Editorial Address
Redfield Community Buckingham Road Winslow BUCKINGHAM MK18 3LZ

Telephone
(0296) 712161

Permaculture Association (Britain)

The Permaculture Association (Britain) is a registered charity (registration no. 290897) that acts as a vehicle for connecting people, ideas, resources and projects in Britain and throughout the world. As well as holding a conference and convergence once a year, its main function is to keep people in touch with one another and facilitate the spreading of information. Membership of the Permaculture Association gives you access to the following:

- Free subscription to *Permaculture Magazine*.
- Local group contacts.
- International contacts.
- Courses – Permaculture courses are held regularly in various parts of Britain:

  Introductory Course – Usually a single weekend. Contains both information and practical work.

  Full Design Course – Comprising 72 hours' teaching. It is the foundation course for those wishing to take up permaculture design work, or implement permaculture in their own homes or on their own land. It is also for those in related professions who wish to add the permacultural perspective to their existing skills. Completion of the design course plus two years' work in permaculture, full or part-time, can lead to the qualification of Diploma in Permaculture Design (Dip. Perm. Des.).

  Specialist Courses – Covering specific subjects in detail.

  Details of current courses are available from the Permaculture Association as well as in *Permaculture Magazine*.

- Permaculture designers – A list of qualified designers is available on request, together with advice on how to choose the one who is right for you and your job.

Address
*The Permaculture Association (Britain)
PO Box 1
Buckfastleigh
Devon
TQ11 0LH*

Telephone
(03643) 333

Publications
Turning Problems into Solutions

Permanent Publications

PERMACULTURE IN A NUTSHELL
by Patrick Whitefield

"A new era requires hard-headed and creative thinking, and you'll find plenty of that in these pages."
Jonathon Porritt
from his preface in *Permaculture in a Nutshell.*

This inspiring book is a concise and accessible introduction to the principles and practice of permaculture in temperate climates.

It explains how it works in the city, the country and on the farm. It also explores ways in which people can work in co-operation to recreate real communities.

Permaculture in a Nutshell clearly describes how we can live fruitfully and sustainably without plundering the Earth, and is essential reading for everyone wishing to find creative solutions for reducing their environmental impact.

Includes useful addresses and further reading lists.

Paperback   96pp   198 x 127mm
ISBN 1 85623 003 1
£4.50 + £0.50 p&p
(Europe p&p: £1.00 / Rest of World p&p: £2.00)

URBAN PERMACULTURE
A Practical Handbook for Sustainable Living
by David Watkins

Urban Permaculture is a do-it-yourself handbook offering many clear and simple steps to small-scale sustainable living. How we grow our food, design our homes and exchange our skills and resources all affect the Earth. This book describes an integrated, ecological approach to living which anyone can practise – in city, town or country – whether we have access to land or not.

Address
*Permanent Publications
Hyden House Ltd
Little Hyden Lane
Clanfield
Hampshire
PO8 0RU*

Telephone
(0705) 596500

Fax
(0705) 595834

Packed with practical information, proven techniques, illustrations and species and plant source lists, *Urban Permaculture* is an invaluable resource for anyone wishing to tread more lightly on the Earth.

Includes information on keeping livestock in a small setting and also useful organisations and further reading lists.

Paperback 160pp 215 x 134mm
ISBN 1 85623 002 3
£7.50 + £1.00 p&p
(Europe p&p: £1.50 / Rest of World p&p: £3.00)

PERMACULTURE MAGAZINE

Permaculture Magazine is a forum of permaculture ideas and practice. Published in Britain, the magazine's emphasis is on permaculture in a temperate climate, including Europe, and is an essential resource for both the established designer and for anyone wishing to live more sustainably.

Containing a wealth of practical information, *Permaculture Magazine* covers a wide spectrum of subjects – from sustainable design and 'how to' information, to the social and economic aspects of creating permanent cultures. It provides access to permaculture design courses and other key resources throughout Britain and the world and it is an important link in the international permaculture network.

Containing 36 pages packed with photographs and illustrations, *Permaculture Magazine* is published quarterly in co-operation with the Permaculture Association (Britain) and is supplied FREE to all its members (*see page 94*).

Full colour cover 297 x 148mm ISSN 0967-5663
£8.00 per 4 issues inc. p&p (U.K. only)
(Europe p&p: £3.00 / Rest of World p&p: £6.00)

Please ask for our FULL CATALOGUE

All publications are available from Permanent Publications (*see page 95 for address*) and are supplied with a full money back guarantee.